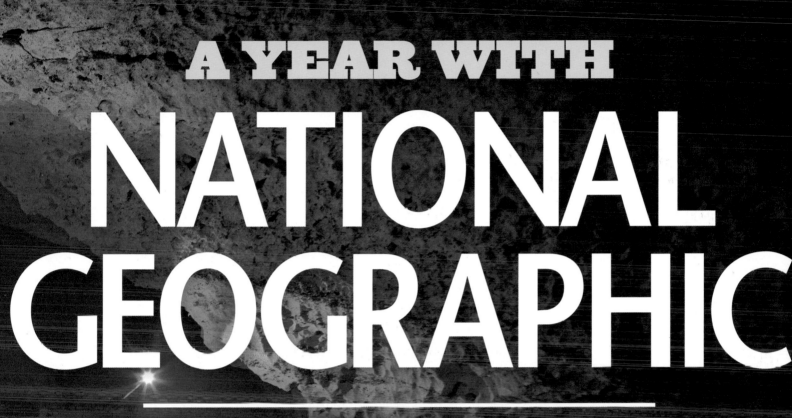

A YEAR WITH
NATIONAL GEOGRAPHIC

YEARBOOK 2015

NATIONAL GEOGRAPHIC

WASHINGTON, D.C.

A riot of colour and dance, Carnaval De Oruro in Bolivia dates back over 2000 years, and is one of South America's most vibrant festivals.

CONTENTS

Foreword *by Janet Goldstein, Senior Vice President and Editorial Director of National Geographic Books* **8**

January *Announced by all the trumpets of the sky / Arrives the snow* **10**

February *O Winter! Frozen pulse and heart of fire* **22**

March *The air is like a butterfly / with frail blue wings* **34**

April *April . . . / Hath put a spirit of youth in everything* **46**

May *May, queen of blossoms, / And fulfilling flowers* **58**

June *It was June, and the world smelled of roses* **70**

July *'Tis summer's very breath / That gently shakes the rustling trees* **82**

August *Oh, the summer night / Has a smile of light / And she sits on a sapphire throne* **94**

September *Silver-misty morning, / Jewelled cobwebs sparkling* **106**

October *Colours burst in wild explosions; / Fiery, flaming shades of fall* **118**

November *The autumn air is clear, / the autumn moon is bright* **130**

December *Frosty days and ice still nights, / Fir trees trimmed with tiny lights* **142**

2015 Calendar **154**

Resources **155**

Illustrations credits **156**

Jade the hedgehog was nearly 11 months old and weighed 450 grams (or 16 ½ oz) when this photograph was taken.

A Year With National Geographic

Welcome to an exciting new year with the *National Geographic Yearbook* for 2015 – packed with fascinating facts, discoveries and stunning images from the realms of nature, science, technology, history, travel, space and beyond. We are thrilled to bring you a year of adventure and insight, sharing highlights and favourite stories from around the world in true National Geographic style.

We've packed this yearbook with breathtaking images by an international team of photographers, as well as spectacular 'Your Shot' images submitted by readers and fans (check out the sandboarder on page 62). Test your knowledge and entertain yourself with fascinating cutting edge news and stories. For example, did you know that there once could have been life on Mars? Or the reason music helps us exercise? How about the physics behind a water slide? Or that dolphins call each other by name?

Each month, you'll find ways to make the National Geographic experience your own. Easy-to-use survival tips prep you for the great outdoors – nearby or far away. A spotlight on amazing animals inspires awe for every species. Whether you're learning local birdcalls or sharing trivia with friends, there's something special for everyone.

As you enjoy this year's *Yearbook,* please know that National Geographic is committed to bringing you the best of the world in words and pictures every day of the year. Happy adventures and best wishes for 2015!

Janet Goldstein

–Janet Goldstein
Senior Vice President and Editorial Director
National Geographic Books

Pictured in the icy grip of winter,
this partially frozen lake is in the
mountainous area northwest of
Japan's capital Tokyo.

ANNOUNCED BY ALL THE TRUMPETS OF THE SKY / ARRIVES THE SNOW

JANUARY

The Pampas

Rub shoulders with the legendary gauchos of Argentina, Chile and Uruguay.

Two gauchos race across a lake near Beron de Astrada in Argentina, in a show of horsemanship for which gauchos are famous.

Cowboys may be rare in the American West, but gauchos still populate vast *estancias,* or ranches, of the grassy pampas of South America. Come summer (winter in the Northern Hemisphere), the best of them compete in *jineteadas* (rodeos) that are such an integral part of life in rural Argentina, Chile and Uruguay.

At these small-town affairs, the gauchos put on a fierce display of horsemanship, whirling *rebenques* (leather whips) overhead and sporting red berets, green scarves and sashes around their waists. 'A gaucho must earn these by being a good rider. And a woman must give you these three things after watching you ride,' explains veteran cowboy Patricio Varcaza.

Afterwards, everyone gathers with the gauchos for a barbecue. The best riders aspire to national rodeos, like January's huge Doma (Rodeo) and Folklore Festival near Cordoba, Argentina. But there, you don't get to have a cookout with the victors. ■

Telltale Tail Wag

Dogs let their tails do the talking. They wag their tails to the right when looking at something they like, such as their owner or a tasty treat. But they wag to the left when they see something to back away from, like an aggressive dog. The responses are a result of the differing roles played by the left and right hemispheres of a dog's brain.

Dolphins Have Names, Respond When Called

Tursiops truncatus
LENGTH: 3–4 m
(10–14 ft)
WEIGHT: 500 kg
(1,100 lb)
GROUP NAME: Pod

Dolphins can help other species in distress and possibly do maths. So it's no surprise that they call each other by 'name'.

Bottlenose dolphins *(Tusiops truncates)* in the Sea of Cortez, Mexico. A new study suggests that dolphins can call to each other individually by using a 'signature whistle'.

Past studies have shown that individual dolphins have a unique whistle, called a 'signature whistle', that they often use in big group settings, like when several pods of dolphins meet at sea. A recent study takes the theory a step further by asserting that a dolphin will respond when it hears the sound of its own signature whistle, repeating that whistle back in a way that seems to say, 'Yup, I'm here – did you call my name?'

Scientists on a boat performed the research on a group of wild dolphins off the coast of eastern Scotland. When one of the dolphins announced itself with its signature whistle – 'I'm Joey!' for example – the researchers recorded that sound. Later, the team played that same 'Joey!' call back to the dolphins and a significant portion of the time, the dolphin they called Joey responded with the same call – as if Joey were saying, 'Yup, I'm here.'

The finding is more evidence that identity is important for dolphins, which form complex relationships within tight-knit communities. The ocean is noisy and visibility is poor, so there's a greater need for sounds that can indicate an animal's identity. ■

STRANGE ... BUT TRUE Bats and dolphins both use echolocation to hunt. This ability is the result of the same genetic mutation, but arose uniquely in each species.

VISIONS OF EARTH

From the ground it's just a queue for a ski lift in Czarna Góra resort, Poland, but viewed from above the skiers become bright brushstrokes on a snowy canvas.

It's in Your Eyes: A Taste for Sweets

A new study reveals that our eyes light up at the prospect of sugary treats, triggered by dopamine released in our brains.

f chocolate brownies put a twinkle in your eyes, there's a chemical reason: Rich, sugary treats trigger a surge of dopamine, the "feel-good" hormone, which can be measured in the retina.

Scientists already knew that light activates dopamine neurons in the retina and that consuming sugar and fat releases dopamine in the so-called midbrain system. But until now, those two activities were thought to be unrelated, says nutritionist and lead researcher Jennifer Nasser. 'Many retinal experts told me that using ERG [electroretinography] in this way probably wouldn't work,' she says, but when she connected the conclusions of several other studies involving dopamine in both the brain and eye, 'it just seemed logical.'

Researchers flashed a light into the eyes of subjects who had consumed one of three different substances: water, chocolate brownies or the drug methylphenidate (Ritalin), which is known to increase dopamine levels in the brain. As the light hit the optic nerve, it triggered electrical signals that could be measured by ERG, indicating how much dopamine was being released.

They found that a mouthful of brownie triggered a spike of dopamine almost identical to the spike caused by the drug, while the water had no noticeable effect. In other words, there's a scientific reason that you want another brownie. The sugar and fat in the brownies probably play a bigger role than the chocolate, Nasser believes – they simply used chocolate brownies in their study because that's what the first subject named as a favourite food. In future studies, she'd like to test responses to other foods and to single ingredients, such as sugar. ▪

The Value of Chocolate
The Maya of Central America first discovered chocolate around 600 A.D., using it as currency and in a delicacy drink called 'chocolatl'.

Sir Nils Olav
The Knighted Penguin

Sir Nils Olav is a king penguin, but he's not really a king, he's a knight. Since 1972, the Norwegian King's Guard – which protects Norway's royal family in times of crisis – has been adopting king penguins as mascots. One reason is that the birds' black-and-white feathers resemble the soldiers' uniforms. Over the years, Nils has been promoted from member to sergeant major to colonel in chief and now to knight.

The penguin was named after two people: Maj. Nils Egelien, who organised his adoption in 1972 and the then King of Norway, King Olav. When Nils was named a knight, the honour was so high that it had to be approved by the royal family, including King Harald V.

Sir Nils lives at the Edinburgh Zoo in Scotland and Norwegian soldiers occasionally come by to say hello. 'Nils instantly recognises the soldiers when they visit,' says penguin keeper Roslin Talbot. 'He waddles over and squawks at them.'

His knighthood ceremony was no different. Before receiving a sword tap on each shoulder, Nils walked past the line of soldiers at attention, occasionally stopping to inspect the troops. He was, as usual, on his best behaviour. All the knighted penguin needs now is a suit of armour. ■

A very prestigious penguin: the only knighted king penguin, Sir Nils Olav, has a distinctly regal air as he inspects his visiting troops at Edinburgh Zoo.

How To: Escape Quicksand

If you fall into quicksand, remember these simple steps. They could save your life!

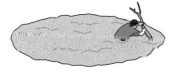
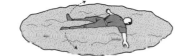

1. Don't struggle. Grab onto any solid branch floating on the quicksand and lie on top of it.

2. If you don't have access to a branch, increase your surface area by arching your back and slowly wriggling your feet apart.

3. Continue leaning back and increasing your surface area until your legs rise to the surface and your body floats on the sand.

4. Slowly work your way back to solid ground by moving one limb at a time, while keeping your body weight distributed.

EXPERT TIP: To move easily in a jungle, you must focus on the jungle farther out and find natural breaks in the foliage. Look *through* the jungle, not *at* it. Stop and bend down occasionally to look along the jungle floor, which may reveal game trails you can follow.

Neanderthals Used Toothpicks

Were Neanderthals merely lumbering oafs? Not as far as dental hygiene is concerned, archaeologists suggest.

Our long-lost *Homo neanderthalensis* cousins used toothpicks to clean their teeth and relieve the pain of gum disease, suggests a team at Spain's Institut Català de Paleoecologia Humana i Evolució Social (IPHES). Their study provides the oldest evidence of toothpick use for the purpose of pain relief. The practice, one suspects, was probably better than using a spear.

Fossil teeth estimated to be 50,000 to 150,000 years old were found at the Cova Foradà site in Valencia, Spain, embedded in the upper jaw of an ancient skull. The teeth were free of cavities, but showed heavy dental wear. This was likely due to a highly abrasive diet that probably included 'stems, fruits, leaves, etc. and a great amount of meat and also marrow,' according to study lead author Marina Lozano. The teeth also showed telltale toothpick marks.

That Neanderthals may have used toothpicks isn't a novel idea. Humans have been picking at their teeth since we've had teeth to pick. Research has shown evidence of toothpick marks as far back as *Homo habilis,* an early human species that lived around 1.7 million years ago. The toothpicks were most likely thin sticks or rigid stalks of grass. For Neanderthals, it was presumably no different.

What's different here is that the new study suggests that Neanderthals were doing more than just de-gunking their molars. The fossils displayed evidence of periodontal disease. That led the researchers to hypothesise that Neanderthals employed toothpicks not just to clean teeth and dislodge food particles but also to help relieve pain and inflammation caused by gum disease.

According to the study, 'The use of toothpicks of plant origin to mitigate sore gums could also be considered as a type of rudimentary dental treatment.' If the toothpick finding bears out, it would be the oldest evidence of palliative dental care of its kind. And it would suggest that the Neanderthal was no technological slouch.

There's even been some evidence that Neanderthals made use of medicinal plants. If accurate, the new findings would contribute to mounting evidence that Neanderthals were more astute than previously realised.

And they probably had brighter smiles, too. ■

Surprise! When modern humans migrated out of Africa, they encountered Neanderthals on the Eurasian continent and produced offspring. Today, the genomes of people living outside Africa are composed of I to 4 percent Neanderthal DNA.

A Neanderthal skull from Wadi Amud, Israel. New research suggests that Neanderthals used toothpicks to clean their teeth and relieve the pain of gum disease.

Appearing to disappear: Artist Liu Bolin is covered in painstakingly painted camouflage, then assistants position his body so that he seems to vanish.

Toasting

The tradition of raising a glass in someone's honour dates back to the ancient Greeks and Romans. In the sixth century B.C., poison was a common way to eliminate enemies; so to show that a beverage was safe to consume, a host would drink to a guest's health by taking the first sip. But it was the Romans who added the actual toast. As a pledge of friendship, they would drop a piece of spiced toast into the communal cup of wine raised at a ceremony, to add a sweet flavour and reduce acidity. The clinking of glasses after a toast emerged in 17th-century England, where is was believed that the bell-like noise banished the devil. ■

Smew

Mergellus albellus

LENGTH: 38–44 cm (15–17 in)

WINGSPAN: 55–68 cm
(22–27 in)

The smew travels in groups, flying quickly and quietly across a wide migratory range. It is a shy bird, easily startled and able to spring into flight quickly from the water, where it feeds on small fish, insects, amphibians and plants. The Smew's black-and-white wings are visible in flight. It nests in tree holes, often using abandoned woodpecker nests on the edges of lakes. ■

Superglue

It might surprise you to know that your mouth may contain superglue – it's become an ingredient in dental fillings. Since its invention in 1942, the amazing adhesive that 'sticks to anything' has become a component of many formulas and has found its way into several less commonly known products. Its properties can be explained in part by the fact that it's a product of covalent bonding, or shared electrons.

Superglue was discovered accidentally when scientists were working to create clear plastic gunsights during World War II. They rejected the material because it stuck to everything. Researchers at Eastman Kodak 'rediscovered' it in 1951 and by 1958 it was on the market as an extra-sticky glue.

The Vietnam War introduced the first medical usage of superglue, to stop soldiers' bleeding in the field until they could be transported for conventional treatment. Its success under emergency conditions eventually led to approval by the U.S. Food and Drug Administration.

By the early 21st century, a medical-grade version of superglue had been created and doctors were using it for suturing and laceration repair. ■

Brazil: A close-up shot of the eye of a toco toucan (*Ramphastos toco albogularis*) taken in the Pantanal, one of the world's largest tropical wetland areas.

FE

O WINTER! FROZEN PULSE AND HEART OF FIRE

BRUARY

Harbin, China

Wander among pagodas in a fairyland of ice and snow.

Harbin, China: As night falls, colourful lights illuminate ice sculptures by local artists, creating a truly magical frozen scene.

W inters are harsh in Heilongjiang, China, and the residents of Harbin, its capital, brighten the long, frigid months by carving fantastical frozen sculptures for the International Ice and Snow Festival in January and February.

Wrap up warm and pull on sturdy boots to explore. Pale winter sunlight sparkles on immense, life-size re-creations of famous landmarks. Tightly packed snow crunches underfoot as you hike to the top of the Athens Acropolis or peer inside the gates of the Forbidden City. Warm up with an exhilarating ride down a giant ice slide on the frozen Songhua River, then watch the island become an otherworldly land of shimmering ice and brilliant colours. As darkness falls, shades of crimson, sapphire and lime green blaze forth from the translucent ice blocks.

'It's quite surreal, due to both the scale and all the lighting – like being in a fantasy movie,' says Christian Stanley of the China Travel Company, which offers tours of the festival. ■

Blame a Bad Night's Sleep on the Moon

Scientists have found evidence that human sleep patterns are timed to the moon's phases. The lunar cycle seems to influence human sleep, even when you don't 'see' it or know what phase it's in. Around the full moon, those in a study took longer to fall asleep, slept for less time and had lowered sleep quality.

Crickets Act Differently With an Audience

Gryllus pennsylvanicus
LENGTH: 1.5–2.5 cm
(0.6–1.0 in)
COLOURS: Black, red, brown
RANGE: North America

Everybody loves an audience – even crickets. A new study shows that male insects are more aggressive when somebody's watching.

Two male spring field crickets fight it out. A new study suggests they will become more aggressive if other crickets are watching.

Cricket behaviour, it seems, 'is much more complex than we give them credit for,' reports Lauren Fitzsimmons, a biologist at the University of Windsor in Ontario, Canada. Experiments conducted by Fitzsimmons and her advisor revealed this grandstanding phenomenon for the first time in invertebrates.

To start, the team caught crickets from local fields and reared their offspring in the laboratory. They then staged a series of trials in which pairs of male crickets were placed into a small arena, which always led to fights.

In a viewing area adjacent to the arena but separated by glass, the scientists placed either a male cricket or female cricket watching and listening to a fight or no audience.

The results showed that all the males fought more violently – and put on more grandiose victory dances – when another cricket, male or female, was present than when they had no audience at all. What's more, wild males responded more strongly overall to an audience than did lab-reared crickets, suggesting that the isolated laboratory insects didn't have enough social exposure to other crickets to know what was going on.

Fitzsimmons suspects there are multiple reasons why the fighting males acted more aggressively with a crowd—mating and social influence, to name a few. ■

STRANGE ... BUT TRUE Some cicadas can produce loud, noisy calls that can be heard up to 1.5 kilometres (1 mile) away.

VISIONS OF EARTH

This illusion of energy was created with an LED light scribbled over the kitchen's surfaces and the figure lying on the floor during a 24-minute exposure.

Decapitated Worms Can Regrow Heads, Keep Old Memories

In French Revolution style, researchers decapitated flatworms – then did something that would give even Madame Defarge the creeps.

The scientists let the worms' heads grow back and found that their memories returned along with the new noggins, according to a recent study.

Michael Levin and Tal Shomrat, biologists at Tufts University in the United States, have been studying how animals store and process information – whether it's memories in the brain or the blueprints for developing organs in the body.

The team turned to flatworms because they have many of the same organs and body organisation as people: a brain and nervous system, bilateral symmetry and even some of the same behaviours. Yet unlike people, these worms have a remarkable ability to regenerate organs and body parts, including their brains – making them perfect research subjects.

Planarian flatworms have primitive eyes that can detect light, which they generally avoid because it exposes them to predators. The researchers retrained the worms to prefer lighted areas by providing food rewards when a worm ventured into bright spots and punishments when it remained in the dark. After the team verified that the worms had memorised where to find food, they chopped off some of the worms' heads and let them regrow.

Next, the team showed the worms with the regrown heads where to find food – essentially a refresher course of their training before decapitation. Subsequent experiments showed that the worms remembered where the light spot was, that it was safe and that food could be found there. The worms' memories were just as accurate as those worms who had never lost their heads.

The obvious question is how can a worm remember things after losing its head? 'We have no idea,' Levin admits. 'What we do know is that memory can be stored outside the brain – presumably in other body cells – so that [memories] can get imprinted onto the new brain as it regenerates.' ■

Lend a Hand
Worms aren't the only regenerative ones out there. Salamanders are known to grow back lost tails, jaws, eyes and even hearts over the course of a few days.

Belle the Beagle

This man really was saved by the Belle.

Belle and her owner, Kevin Weaver, pose for a photo after her award ceremony.

When Belle, a beagle, found her owner Kevin Weaver unconscious on his kitchen floor in the midst of a diabetic seizure, her training kicked in. She managed to locate his mobile phone and make an emergency, lifesaving phone call by biting down on the keypad.

Emergency operators were able to make out only the sounds of the beagle barking on the other end of the line and decided that was enough to send help. Hours later, Kevin awoke in the hospital and Belle, of course, was right by his side.

Belle had been trained as a medical assistance dog. She was able to recognise the warning signs for her owner's diabetes and would occasionally take readings by licking Weaver's nose to test his blood-sugar levels. Part of her training also included biting down on a phone key preprogrammed to call the emergency services in a worst-case scenario.

In 2006, Belle became the first animal to receive the VITA Wireless Samaritan Award in a ceremony in Washington, D.C. The award is given to individuals who use their mobile phones in an emergency situation to save a life, prevent crime or help in an emergency. ■

How To: Build a Snow Trench

Even in the tropics, mountains can be icy.

1 Using a shovel, pot, stick, or whatever is available, dig a trench in snow at least 1.5 metres (5 feet) deep. Keep the loose snow in a pile next to the trench.

2 Make the trench long and wide enough to lie down and at least a metre (3 feet) deep to take advantage of the snow's insulating properties. Lay a tarp, branches or pine needles on the bottom so you're not lying directly on snow.

3 Criss-cross branches and pine boughs across the top, leaving an entry hole (downwind).

4 Using excavated snow, make a low snow mound on top of the covered support. Pull a branch over the door, but allow ventilation.

EXPERT TIP: Always monitor weather forecasts in the days leading up to your departure. Use your best weather sense in the field, too, to avoid getting caught by surprise in dangerous conditions.

Why Did Penguins Stop Flying?

Penguins' swimming prowess cost them their ability to fly, a new study says.

Flight might make some aspects of penguins' Antarctic life much easier. The gruelling march of the emperor penguins, for example, might take only a few easy hours rather than many deadly days. Escaping such predators as leopard seals at the water's edge would also be easier if penguins could take flight, so scientists have often wondered why and how the birds lost that ability.

A popular theory of biomechanics suggests that the birds' once-flight-adapted wings simply became more and more efficient for swimming and eventually lost their ability to get penguins off the ground. The enhanced diving capability was more beneficial, increasing the opportunities to forage for food at depth. A modern emperor penguin can hold its breath for more than 20 minutes and quickly dive to 450 metres (1,500 feet) to feast.

'Clearly, form constrains function in wild animals and movement in one medium creates trade-offs with movement in a second medium,' notes Kyle Elliott of the University of Manitoba, co-author of the study. 'Bottom line is that good flippers don't fly very well.'

A thorough analysis of how diving birds burn energy reveals why today's penguins are grounded. 'Basically the birds do only three things: sit, swim and fly. So by measuring lots of birds and combining their time budgets with the total costs of living from the isotope measures, it is possible to calculate how much each component of the budget costs,' explains study co-author John Speakman, who leads the Energetics Research Group at the University of Aberdeen, Scotland.

Scientists don't have fossils of flighted penguin ancestors; the earliest known penguin dates to just after the Cretaceous-Tertiary boundary (60 to 58 million years ago). But bigger bodies boost dive efficiency and allow for longer dives, which may be why rapid evolution produced so many bigger-bodied penguins soon after the animals lost the ability to fly.

In nature, such adaptations happen for good reason, typically related to survival and reproduction. When mammals, the ancestors of today's dolphins and whales, took to the sea, competition for resources intensified. The penguins' new deep-diving abililty allowed them to beat diving birds and aquatic mammals alike. ■

Flightless but Still Fast
The ostrich is the world's largest flightless bird and one of the fastest runners in the animal kingdom. Ostriches may use their wings as 'rudders' to help them change direction while running.

Salisbury Plain, South Georgia: An orderly line of king penguins walks towards the camera against a backdrop of mountains and icebergs in the remote southern Atlantic Ocean.

EDITOR'S PICK

Extreme selfie: Russian photographer Kirill Oreshkin has earned the nickname 'the Russian Spiderman' for scaling tall buildings armed only with a camera.

Soap

The very first cleansing agents came from plants; in the second millennium B.C., the Hittites of Asia Minor washed themselves with water and ashes from the soapwort plant, which contains a natural cleansing agent called saponin.

But soap as we know it came along about 600 B.C., thanks to the seafaring Phoenicians of the eastern Mediterranean Sea. They developed a waxy substance made by boiling ashes, water and goat fat. What remained after evaporation was soap. By about 800 A.D., soapmaking had become a European craft, with Spain one of the preeminent manufacturers. In 1879, the popular floating Ivory soap was invented by accident when a worker forgot to turn off a mixing vat. Too much air was added, and the product was a hit. ■

Bewick's Swan

Cygnus columbianus

LENGTH: 115–140 cm (45–55 in)
WINGSPAN: 168–211 cm (66–83 in)

A noisy, high-pitched whooping is the call of this elegant aquatic bird. An exceptionally fast swimmer, Bewick's swan uses its long neck to feed on submerged vegetation while keeping its body upright. Flocks of swans migrate thousands of kilometres between breeding grounds in the Arctic and temperate wintering areas. ■

Home Plumbing Systems

Plumbing is one of those marvels of modern living. But how does water rise to a home's upper floors to flow at the turn of a tap? In a word: pressure.

The flow is generated by exploiting Pascal's insight that water pressure increases with depth, not overall volume. Water towers achieve this depth through elevation. The weight of the water column pushes downward, pressing water through supply lines with enough force to lift it to upper floors. But by the same effect, people on the ground floor usually get better water pressure than people on the higher floors.

Wastewater leaves the home via a separate system that also depends on gravity. All pipes are angled to let the water drain down.

Among common plumbing fixtures, the humble toilet is probably the most elaborate. It flushes by a siphon effect. Push the flush handle and a chain lifts open a valve in the toilet tank, dumping water into the bowl. The water enters quickly enough to flood the toilet's drainpipe, which curves up and then down as it leaves the bowl. As in any siphon, the flow downward creates a low-pressure area at the top of the pipe's curve, which sucks the rest of the water from the bowl, emptying it into the waste stream. ■

Nandgaon, India: Hindu devotees participate in rituals for the Lathmar Holi festival at the Nandji Temple. Lathmar Holi is a local celebration that takes place a few days before the national Holi day on 27 March.

THE AIR IS LIKE A BUTTERFLY / WITH FRAIL BLUE WINGS

MARCH

Teotihuacan, Mexico

Renew the spirit and watch the sun rise over ancient ruins.

Teotihuacan, Mexico: Musicians dressed in traditional Indian costume are among those who gather at the Teotihuacan ruins to celebrate the arrival of spring.

Thousands gather atop the Pyramid of the Sun in mid-March, awaiting daybreak at Teotihuacan, the ancient ruins in the northern outskirts of Mexico City. Many are clad in white; some have brought crystals and amulets to capture the energy of the rising sun. When the orb finally rises over the Sierra Madre, people start to chant, sing and pray, raising their arms to welcome the vernal equinox.

Visitors will find the experience indelible. For Mexicans, the celebration 'connects them to their past, their history and their family,' explains Kenneth Fagan, who filmed the rites for Arizona State University.

The communal ambience invites everyone to participate. Join Aztec dancers and other troupes from all around Mexico. Munch freshly made tamales or bargain for trinkets with the many wandering vendors. Inhale the brusque aroma of the copal incense burned by those who believe in the ancient gods. Get your fortune told by a shaman. And maybe have evil spirits exorcised by *brujos* (witches), on hand just in case the future doesn't look bright. ■

Panda Poo Transforms Plants Into Fuel

Microbes may help the process of breaking down plants to produce biofuels quickly, and the bacteria that dwell within pandas' guts might be especially effective at this task. After all, the tiny organisms can handle the 9 to 18 kilograms (20–40 lb) of bamboo an adult panda consumes each day.

Sabre-toothed Tigers Had a Surprisingly Weak Bite

Smilodon fatalis
STATUS: Extinct
WEIGHT: 160–270 kg (360–600 lb)
RANGE: North America

At least two species of sabre-toothed cats were more muscle than bite, subduing their prey with powerful necks and forelimbs, a new study says.

The sabre-toothed tiger actually used its powerful neck muscles to drive its huge teeth into its prey, rather than its jaw muscles like modern-day lions.

The long-fanged prehistoric predators have long intrigued both the scholarly and public imagination, particularly in regard to their hunting technique. One question scientists have paid particular attention to is whether the cats ran down prey like lions today do, dispatching them with a powerful bite to the throat.

Ongoing research has suggested not. A 2007 study found that North America's saber-toothed cat *Smilodon fatalis* was a wimpy biter when compared with modern-day lions. A computer model based on fossil skulls shows that both *Smilodon* and a 'bizarre', distantly related sabretooth species, *Thylacosmilus atrox*, had weak jaws but extremely strong neck muscles, which they used to sink their long teeth deep into flesh, according to the study.

The finding sheds light on the evolution of this killing method – one that's arisen several times over the history of life on Earth, said study co-author Lawrence Witmer, a palaeontologist at Ohio University. Researchers looked at the head-depressing muscles – which run from the neck to the head and drive the head down – and determined that the animals weren't biting down on prey. Rather, they were driving the teeth into the prey using their neck muscles. ■

STRANGE ... BUT TRUE Which has a stronger bite: a dog, a lion or a *Tyranno-saurus rex*? *T. rex* takes the cake with a chomp of 35,000 to 57,000 newtons.

VISIONS OF EARTH

Rio de Janeiro, Brazil:
Samba muses from the
Beija-Flor samba school
parade from podiums on one
of the school's impressive
floats at the famous Sambo-
dromo during Rio's Carnival.

What a Day for a Daydream

Whether it's worrying or fantasising, all of us daydream – letting our minds escape from the task at hand.

Before you drift off into la-la land, here are some interesting facts about daydreaming you may not have known.

You daydream less as you get older. Daydreaming is often about anticipating the future, especially in a fantasy context. But as people get older, the amount of time they spend daydreaming decreases – perhaps as the future shrinks.

Daydreaming makes you forget what you were doing. If people are asked to daydream about the past, for instance, they tend to forget what they were doing before the daydream started, research shows. The type of daydream also affects how much you forget. When people working on a task were asked to daydream about their childhood home, older subjects forgot more of the interrupted task than younger subjects did. The more difficult to remember the daydream subject is, the bigger the forgetting effect.

Daydreaming turns off other parts of the brain. Our brain has two key systems: an analytic part that helps us make reasoned decisions and an empathetic part that allows us to relate to others. When you are daydreaming, your mind naturally cycles through different modes of thinking and during this time the analytic and empathetic parts of your brain tend to turn each other off.

Daydreaming makes you more creative. Many times the 'dialogue' that occurs when the daydreaming mind cycles through different parts of the brain accesses information that was dormant or out of reach. In addition, the daydreaming mind may make an association between bits of information that the person had never considered in that particular way. ■

Flex Your Muscles
Exercise can ramp up your creativity and bring you back to Earth from an engaging daydream. Studies have shown that a moderate amount of aerobic activity is enough to stimulate your brain.

Ayumu the Chimp
Memory Master

Ayumu is a chimpanzee who lives at the Primate Research Institute of Kyoto University in Japan. Ayumu, one of 14 chimpanzees spanning three generations at the institute, has learned the sequence of numbers 1 to 19 and can point to them in ascending order, which is a first for chimpanzees.

Another amazing skill Ayumu has is to watch numbers 1 to 9 appear in random locations on screen and then recall precisely where the numbers appeared – all in 60 milliseconds. It's an ability that few—if any—humans have. Ayumu's skills were on display at the 2013 annual meeting of the American Association for the Advancement of Science (AAAS).

The institute's director, Tetsuro Matsuzawa, has been studying chimpanzee intelligence for more than 30 years and describes the chimps as his 'research partners'. It is apparent that out of all the chimps, it is Ayumu whose intelligence really shines. An adept short-term memory is important for

Ayumu the chimpanzee performs a memory test with randomly placed consecutive Arabic numerals which he then accurately replicates on a touch screen computer in Kyoto, Japan.

chimpanzee survival in the wild, as they are often presented with situations in which they need to make quick, meaningful decisions. ■

How To: Sun-dry Meat
A little jerky never hurt anyone.

1 Cut the meat into long, thin strips. Aim for a half-centimetre (quarter-inch) thickness.

2 String a cord between two supports, out of reach of animals.

3 Skewer pieces of meat on the cord or drape them over it. Keep the pieces from touching each other, or from touching themselves if folded.

4 Depending on the thickness of the meat, the process can take anything from a few hours to two days.

EXPERT TIP: If in the desert, wait until after the heat of the day to make a cooking fire, and then only if necessary. Nighttime blazes provide warmth and can serve as a long-distance signal.

The Atlantic Ocean May Dry Up in 200 Million Years

A newly discovered crack in the Earth's crust could pull North America and Europe together.

A new map of the seafloor off the coast of Portugal has revealed what could be the birth of a new subduction zone. Subduction zones occur when tectonic plates – the large rock slabs that make up the Earth's crust – crash into one another. The edge of the heavier plate slides, or 'subducts', below the lighter plate. It then melts back into the Earth's mantle, the layer just below the crust.

Over the past 20 years, several scientific teams from different countries have launched research cruises to map the seafloor off Portugal to look for proof that a new subduction zone was forming. Scientists gathered data from different mapping projects and combined them to create the new tectonic map of the seafloor. The updated map provided the first conclusive proof that the ocean floor here is indeed beginning to fracture and that a new subduction zone is starting to form.

The newly discovered subduction zone is located in the Atlantic Ocean about 200 kilometres (120 mi) off southwestern Portugal. It is made up of six distinct segments that together span a distance of about 300 kilometres (185 miles).

The development of this new subduction zone could signal the start of an extended cycle that fuses continents together into a single landmass – or 'supercontinent' – and pushes out our oceans. This break-up and reformation of supercontinents has happened at least three times during Earth's approximately four-billion-year history.

The subduction zone is actually a recently formed crack in the Eurasian plate, one of about a dozen tectonic plates that make up the Earth's crust. The Eurasian plate contains all of Europe and most of Asia. If it grows, the Eurasian plate could eventually split into separate oceanic and continental sections. The oceanic section – which is made of denser rock – would then dive beneath the continental section, causing the Atlantic Ocean to shrink, pulling North America and Europe closer together. ■

Moving Mountains The Himalayan mountain range formed in a tectonic subduction event around 20 million years ago, when the Indo-Australian plate and the Eurasian plate collided. The Himalayas continue to rise by an average of 2 centimetres (0.8 in) each year.

One tectonic plate sliding under another in the Atlantic Ocean could begin pulling Europe and America together, creating a single landmass in 200 million years' time.

Fit to burst: this high-speed photograph captures an orange water balloon in the instant that it begins to explode.

Marbles

A children's toy for millennia, marbles have been discovered in prehistoric caves. These baked clay marbles were of uncertain purpose, but it is known that adults in almost every early culture used them for religious ceremonies. At some point, they evolved into toys; the earliest known of these presumed toys dates back to 3000 B.C.

The Romans made marbles from clear glass. Celtic, Saxon and African tribes made marbles from organic matter like olives, nuts and fruit pits. In a game from 17th-century England, a player had to shoot from the exact place where his marble landed, sometimes requiring that he use his knuckles for support in an awkward position. The term 'knuckle down', meaning to apply oneself diligently to a task, most likely comes from this game. ■

European Turtle Dove

Sterptopelia turtur

LENGTH: 24–29 cm (9.5–11.5 in)
RANGE: Breeds in Europe, migrates to Africa
WINGSPAN: 47–53 cm (18.5–21.0 in)

From biblical verses to Shakespeare's poems, turtle doves are often celebrated as symbols of devotion. Smaller than other doves, the European turtle dove can be found in open, sunny areas, feeding on seeds, shoots and insects. Its name comes from the soft *turr-turr* call that it makes in short intervals. ■

Allergies

If you have allergies, you have an overactive immune system. When you inhale grass pollen, for example, your immune cells identify the pollen as a foreign invader and produce immunoglobulin E (IgE) antibodies specific to this particular antigen. These antibodies bind to receptors on special immune cells called mast cells, found in connective tissue and mucous membranes and basophils, a type of white blood cell that circulates in blood. As a result, you become sensitised to the grass pollen.

The next time you encounter the pollen, its antigen attaches to matched antibodies already on the surfaces of your mast and basophil cells. Proteins in your blood are drawn to the bonded antibody–antigen complex and, step by step, assemble into a cell-puncturing cylinder. This process disrupts the outer membrane of the immune cell, which releases histamine, serotonin, heparin and other chemicals. Depending on the area of the body affected, these chemicals can produce swelling, itching, sneezing, vomiting and diarrhea, airway spasm and dilation of blood vessels. Meanwhile, the immune cells also give off chemical signals telling other immune cells to make more IgE. ■

Ninh Diem, Vietnam: Workers in the salt fields at dawn gather large loads of salt left when seawater trapped in shallow pools evaporates.

APRIL . . . / HATH PUT A SPIRIT OF YOUTH IN EVERYTHING

APRIL

Victoria Falls, Zambia and Zimbabwe

Marvel at the world's 'greatest sheet of falling water'.

A rainbow hangs over the majestic beauty of Victoria Falls, described by UNESCO as the Earth's 'greatest sheet of falling water'.

'Scenes so lovely must have been gazed upon by angels in their flight,' said Scottish explorer David Livingstone, bringing Victoria Falls poetically to the attention of the outside world. Described by the UNESCO World Heritage Committee as Earth's 'greatest sheet of falling water,' the falls are at their most thunderous around April and May, after the rainy season. To stand in front of the mighty cascade, 90 metres (300 ft) high and 1.6 kilometres (1 mi) wide, is to experience the combined power of geology, vast amounts of water and time.

Victoria Falls straddles the Zambia-Zimbabwe border and each country claims the best views. But visitors don't need to choose sides – it's easy enough to walk across the border and do both. Even better, a bird's-eye perspective from high above avoids the argument altogether. One option is an open aircraft ride, where passengers feel the wind in their hair as they take in the unforgettable sight of the Zambezi River, Livingstone Island and wildlife on surrounding plains that stretch to the horizon. ■

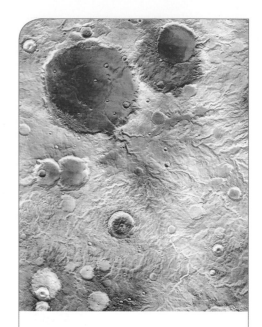

Dreaming of a White Mars

Computer models of the Martian atmosphere suggest evidence for ancient snow on the planet's higher elevations. Models suggest that Mars never got warm enough for rain, so evidence for snowmelt is compelling. A few centimetres (an inch or two) of run-off may have flowed down steep slopes every day for many millions of years.

Fruits and Vegetables Can Defend Themselves

The next time you wander among the produce in your local market, consider this: those fruits and veggies are still alive. Though they may not be able to move, research shows that these plants can still protect themselves.

Can your carrots tell the time? Up to a week after they were picked, a study found that vegetables were still responding to light/dark cycles.

Research shows that some vegetables and fruits exhibit circadian rhythms and can adjust their defensive compounds and nutrients accordingly. A study found that store-bought produce responded to light/dark cycles up to about a week after harvest. When the produce was kept on the same light/dark cycle as a predator – in this case, cabbage looper moth caterpillars – it was better able to resist attacks.

Circadian 'clocks' tell plants when the seasons change by the variations in day length, but the clock is also critical in plant defences against insects. The plants 'know when the insects eat,' says Janet Braam, a co-author on the recent study, 'so they can prepare a defence in advance.'

Braam 'trained' store-bought cabbage by exposing the samples to equal hours of light and dark for three days. The researchers then exposed the vegetables to cabbage looper moth caterpillars that had been trained to the same cycle. They found that cabbage on the same schedule as the caterpillars marshalled its defences in time and suffered the least amount of damage from the insect, while cabbage samples out of sync with the caterpillars' schedule lost 20 times more tissue to the hungry herbivores. ■

STRANGE ... BUT TRUE A man in the U.K. grew a giant courgette that weighed as much as a large sheepdog.

VISIONS OF EARTH

Berndnaut Smilde uses moisture, smoke and dramatic lighting to fleetingly make indoor nimbuses, like this one in a castle near Lanaken, Belgium.

Nature Glows With Neon Plants and Animals

I scream, you scream, we all scream for . . . glow-in-the-dark ice cream?

This glow-in-the-dark ice cream uses synthesised jellyfish luminescence that reacts with the eater's tongue's neutral pH to light up when it is licked.

British boutique ice cream maker Lick Me I'm Delicious (yes, that is the company's real name) has released an ice cream that contains a luminescent protein from glowing jellyfish. The idea? Lick the ice cream and the calcium-activated proteins react by glowing, thanks to differences in pH between your mouth and the ice cream. But no worries: Charlie Harry Francis, the food scientist who invented the treat, assures foodies that it's safe for consumption.

Mushrooms. Deep in the Brazilian rainforest is a 'shroom named after the verse about eternal light in Mozart's Requiem *(Mycena luxaeterna)*. The otherworldly glow probably helps these mushrooms grab dinner – with the help of a sticky gel that lines its stem. Insects fly over, get stuck and become a meal.

Reefs. Special proteins in the reefs of the Pacific Ocean's Solomon Islands create a spectrum of neon shades. The process is called biofluorescence and it makes for more than a light show – doctors hope that these bright proteins can be used to understand the inner workings of the brain.

Animals. Scientists have cloned sheep and cats and made them glow in the dark. Researchers hope that these luminous insects will (literally) illuminate answers to degenerative muscular disorders and other genetic diseases. An otherwise mundane millipede from California is one animal that glows naturally – as a defence mechanism. Scientists think that the millipedes glow to defend themselves against predators in the same way many animals use bright colouration to declare danger. The irony? The multilegged bug is blind. ■

When the Lights Go Out
For deep-sea creatures there's no way to brighten things up unless you do it yourself, and many have evolved ways to create their own glow.

Eddie the Goat and Gerald the Giraffe

Unlikely Animal Friends

When Eddie the goat is harassed by the zebras at the wildlife sanctuary where he lives, his best friend sticks up for him. Charging the zebras, Gerald the giraffe chases them away so the goat can come back and play.

'As our only giraffe, we worried that Gerald would be lonely,' says Chris Wilkinson, head keeper at the Noah's Ark Zoo Farm in Bristol. 'Eddie is a particularly friendly goat, so we moved him into the giraffe house.'

Soon the giraffe and goat became best friends. Sometimes Gerald would lean over to lick the goat's head. Eddie often wrapped his legs around the giraffe's long neck and rubbed him with his head. Though it was meant to be a short-term solution, Eddie and Gerald have stayed together for years, despite the obvious height differences. And they're a huge hit with the zoo's visitors.

Luckily Eddie isn't the jealous type; he even acted like a wingman for Gerald when the zoo got a female giraffe named Genevieve. The goat was friendly with the new giraffe and soon Gerald warmed up to her, too. Now Gerald and Genevieve have a son, George. ■

Not such an odd couple: Gerald the giraffe with his best friend and wingman, outgoing goat Eddie at Noah's Ark Zoo Farm in Bristol

How To: Make a Flotation Device

If you find yourself overboard, an ordinary pair of trousers can make an impromptu flotation device.

1 Hold your breath and remove your trousers, one leg at a time. Tie a knot at the bottom of each leg, while continuously treading water.

2 Holding the waistband open, sling the trousers from behind your head to slam the open waistband on the water before you. This forces air into the legs.

3 Hold the waistband shut in front of you.

4 Let the legs deploy under your armpits and behind you like armbands. When the air seeps out of the trousers, repeat steps 2 to 4.

EXPERT TIP: Surviving along the shore is different from open-sea survival. Food and water are more abundant and shelter is obviously easier to locate or construct. If you decide to travel it is better to move along the coast than to go inland.

Solar Eclipse Myths From Around the World

People around the world, and through time, have come up with tales to explain the sun's disappearance.

'If you do a worldwide survey of eclipse lore, the theme that constantly appears . . . is it's always a disruption of the established order,' observes E. C. Krupp, director of the Griffith Observatory in Los Angeles. 'People depend on the sun's movement,' Krupp explains. '[It's] regular, dependable, you can't tamper with it. And then, all of a sudden . . . time is out of joint. The sun and moon do something that they shouldn't be doing.'

What that disruption means depends on the culture. Some see it as a time of terror, while others look at a solar eclipse as part of the natural order that deserves respect, or as a time of reflection and reconciliation.

Many cultures explain eclipses, both solar and lunar, as a time when demons or animals consume the sun or the moon, says Krupp. As an example, the Griffith Observatory astronomer notes, 'The Vikings saw a pair of sky wolves chasing the sun or the moon.' Whenever one of the wolves caught either of the shining orbs, an eclipse would result. In Vietnam, a frog eats the moon or the sun, while people of the Kwakiutl tribe on the western coast of Canada believe that the mouth of heaven consumes the sun during an eclipse.

One of the more colourful stories involves the Hindu demon Rahu, who disguised himself as a god in order to steal an elixir that grants immortality. The sun and moon saw what Rahu was up to and they reported his crime to the god Vishnu. 'Vishnu slices off his head before [the elixir] can slide past his throat,' says Krupp. As a consequence, Rahu's head became immortal but his body died. The demon's head continues to move through the sky, chasing the sun and the moon out of hatred. Every now and then he catches them and swallows them, but since Rahu has no body, the sun and the moon fall back out.

The Navajo regard the cosmic order of the universe as being all about balance. Some Navajo still observe traditions associated with an eclipse by staying inside with their family, singing songs and refraining from eating, drinking or sleeping.

Eclipses are something Krupp experiences as often as he can. 'They're a chance to see the universe working,' he explains. 'It's the solar system doing its thing right before your eyes and it's a deep and personal pleasure.' ■

Eclipse Safety Tips
During a partial solar eclipse, where only a portion of the sun is covered, our nearest star is still too bright for our eyes to handle. Using filters like welder's glass or a pinhole camera make it easy to see without getting hurt.

An onlooker witnesses an annular solar eclipse. This eerie astronomical phenomenon has inspired folk stories in countries around the world.

An eggs-act science: two hands
are pictured reflecting in the
shiny surface of an egg yolk.

Applause

Romans applauded speeches and dramatic performances they liked and actors sometimes told the audience to 'clap your hands' or express appreciation 'in the usual manner' at the end of a play. University students, whose hands were occupied with notes, complimented good lectures by stamping their feet.

A different kind of applause developed in British parliamentary institutions. Those who approved of what a speaker was saying would often shout, 'Hear him! Hear him!' This was directed at people who might not be paying attention. A shortened form evolved and today we still use 'Hear! Hear!' to voice praise for a speech. ■

Corncrake

Crex crex

LENGTH: 27–30 cm (10.5–12.0 in)
WINGSPAN: 42–53 cm (16.5–21.0 in)

The corncrake is an elusive bird, often hidden in vegetation at its breeding grounds. A mostly solitary bird, the corncrake is easily identified by the loud *krek-krek* call of the males. A fast runner, it prefers to stay on the ground, where it can forage for insects and earthworms. The corncrake will take wing if startled, despite its weak wings. In flight, its bright chestnut wings and trailing legs are unmistakable. ■

Robotic Surgery

The delicate, high-stakes job of performing surgery doesn't seem the most likely candidate for mechanisation. But there are certain things robots can do that even the most skilled surgeon cannot: they can see inside the patient at high magnification and perform tiny movements there with zero tremor. Plus, they never get tired.

Introduced in the 1980s, robot-assisted surgery is increasingly used today in prostate surgery, gynaecologic surgeries and heart surgeries, including coronary bypass and mitral valve repair. The surgeon sits at a computer console that operates a separate unit consisting of robotic arms and a high-definition camera.

Robotic surgery is available at some of the most advanced surgery centres. Many people claim that it allows accurate, minimal movements that mean a quicker and less painful recovery for the patient. But the approach is controversial. Some surgeons argue that while robotic assistance is beneficial in cases where they'd otherwise have to make a large incision, there's little evidence that it's better for patients than ordinary surgery by an experienced surgeon. ■

Namibia, Africa: Two elephants affectionately play together in Etosha National Park, a 22,270-square-kilometre (8,600 sq mi) area in the country's northwest.

MAY, QUEEN OF BLOSSOMS, / AND FULFILLING FLOWERS

MAY

Monte Carlo, Monaco

Speed and glamour mix along the French Riviera.

Monte Carlo, Monaco: City driving takes on a whole new meaning as the Monaco Grand Prix roars around Monte Carlo's narrow streets.

It's not the screaming metal demons that make the Monaco Grand Prix such a singular motor racing experience, it's the ability of mere mortals to walk the track – and perhaps mingle casually with the world's greatest drivers – just hours before and after the furious Formula One action each May.

The whole of race week in the tiny principality is that way. You might find yourself sitting next to racing champ Sebastian Vettel at the trackside Chez Bacco restaurant. Or sharing elbow room at the bar with Will Smith in the posh La Rascasse night-club, a favourite with drivers and celebrities who populate the annual race turned see-and-be-seen event.

Get a feel for the 3.2-kilometre (2 mi) course by walking or cycling the sinuous street circuit on one of those blue-sky spring days that add to Monte Carlo's glitter. Then watch Sunday's race from a private terrace perched high above the track – sipping Dom Pérignon, of course, because during race week in Monaco, only the best will do.

Germs Prefer a Handshake

What started as a joke turned into a scientific study: fist-bumping reduces the transmission of bacteria by about four times, compared with shaking hands. If you shake someone's hand, you then eat with that part of the hand. Fist-bumping protects the palm's surface from bacteria – though you should still wash your hands and limit exposure.

Orchid Mantis Mimics Flower to Trick Prey

Hymenopus coronatus
LENGTH: 2.5–6.0 cm
(1.0–2.4 in)
RANGE: Southeast
Asia
HABITAT: Rainforest

It may look pretty, but this 'orchid' actually has a trick up its, well, leaves: it's actually a praying mantis trying to get a meal. Researchers are trying to discover the secret to the orchid mantis' convincing camouflage.

In 1879, Australian journalist James Hingsley came back from Indonesia with tales of a carnivorous orchid that enveloped butterflies in its petals and ate them. Hingsley hadn't actually discovered an insect-eating flower, though. He, like the butterflies, had been fooled by the orchid mantis.

Scientists James O'Hanlon and Marie Herberstein of Macquarie University in Australia and Gregory Holwell of the University of Auckland in New Zealand went to Malaysia to see if the orchid mantis's ruse really lured pollinators to their deaths.

The research team observed orchid mantises in the field, counting the number of insects that were attracted to the 'flower'. They compared this to the number of insects that inspected an actual flower in the same amount of time and were surprised to find that the mantises attracted more insects than the real flowers. Other animals use camouflage to hide among flowers, then ambush their prey, but the predatory strategy of the orchid mantis is as unique as it is pretty. ■

An orchid mantis poses as a harmless flower in order to trap unsuspecting insects that land on it in search of pollen.

STRANGE ... BUT TRUE The orchid mantis isn't the only master of disguise. The fly orchid's petals resemble a housefly, because it relies on the insects for pollination.

VISIONS OF EARTH

It's not easy climbing a steep, sandy desert dune, but around 300 people a month make the trek in Swakopmund, Namibia for the novelty of 'sandboarding'.

Why Some Animals Mate Themselves to Death

Is sex worth dying for? For a few male marsupial species, it is – when they know their offspring will survive, a recent study says.

While very rare among mammals, so-called semelparity, or suicidal reproduction, is common in nature. Many plants – including all grains, many vegetables and all plants that live just a year – reproduce this way, as do salmon, insects and some frogs and lizards. Just four mammal species are known to reproduce this way, however, and all are rare marsupials. These dads die after devoting all their resources and energy to mating, an effort that helps their sperm – and genes – win out.

Since the 1970s, scientists have suspected that females synchronise mating so that they wean their young at the same time that insect abundance peaks each year. During that shortened, frenzied mating period, competition to mate with the females and methods of doing so are taken to extremes.

Ecologist Diana Fisher of the University of Queensland in Australia and colleagues seem to have proved parts of this theory with widespread data on species across Australia, Papua New Guinea and South America. 'The frenzied mating season

Found on the east coast of Australia, the dusky antechinus is a marsupial that has a short, intense mating season.

lasts only a couple of weeks,' notes Fisher, 'and males usually die before young are born.' Males produce as many sperm as they can and then disperse as many of them as they can by mating with as many females as possible. 'Males with larger testes, better quality sperm and better endurance succeed in more fertilisations in competition with the sperm of other males when females mate with multiple males,' Fisher concludes.

The study's results suggest that the male marsupials that are most efficient at mating by suicide outcompete other males, which makes dying worthwhile. Either way, while the system seems to work out badly for males, it appears to benefit both the next generation and the females. ■

Swimming Upstream
Salmon are born in fresh water and then journey out to sea after they mature. When it's time to reproduce they return upriver, where they spawn and die.

Alyna the Rabbit

Rabbit Joins Hospital Staff

At ALYN Hospital in Jerusalem, Alyna the rabbit uses her own disabilities to help inspire children to overcome theirs.

Calling Dr. Rabbit! When six-year-old Mussa, who has trouble walking, refused to wear his scary-looking leg braces, the staff at ALYN Hospital in Jerusalem brought in Alyna the rabbit. Her back legs don't work and she wears braces, too. When Mussa saw a rabbit wearing braces, he wanted to as well. Now they race the hospital hallways together.

Alyna was born with her back legs paralyzed. So, owner Riki Yahalom Arbel, a therapist at the hospital, fitted the rabbit with a miniature skateboard-like brace. The bunny pulls herself forward with her front legs while her back legs roll along. With her brace, Alyna has full mobility and lives a normal life.

Arbel figured that the rabbit's disability might help encourage patients who were mobility challenged. She was right. When kids like Mussa see how the rabbit moves, they want to wear their braces. 'The kids take turns strapping Alyna onto her "skateboard", and she loves it,' says Cathy Lanyard, executive director of the American Friends of ALYN Hospital. 'She's like part of the staff – but she gets paid in unlimited snacks and plenty of hugs.'

ALYN Hospital treats 11,000 children a year. In her time there, Alyna has brought plenty of smiles and inspired hundreds of children. ■

How To: Make a Deadfall Trap

A well-made trap can be an important source of food.

1 Find three sticks, roughly the same size. One will be upright, one diagonal and one horizontal. Upright stick: Make a notch in the centre and sharpen the top end. Diagonal stick: Carve a notch near one end and sharpen the other end. Horizontal stick: Carve a slot in the centre and make a notch near the top end.

2 Assemble: Drive the upright stick into the ground. Insert the horizontal stick into the notch on the upright and the diagonal stick onto the top of the upright. Insert the diagonal stick's pointed end into the notch on the horizontal stick. Place bait on the free end of the horizontal stick and balance a weight on top of the diagonal stick, which is poised over the bait.

EXPERT TIP: Do not assume that because one part of a plant is edible, other parts are too. Likewise, do not assume that if cooked plant matter is edible, the raw plant must be as well, or vice versa.

How Music Helps Us Exercise

A good song can make your workout harder, better, faster, stronger.

Several years ago, cognitive scientist Tom Fritz spent time in northern Cameroon observing the Mafa people, who have some fascinating musical rituals. The Mafa language doesn't have a word for music, because it is always intertwined with specific rituals, like preparing for the harvest. Men stand in a circle and play wooden flutes. Some dance and run while playing, and the rituals often last several hours. 'It's physically very exhausting,' Fritz says. 'They achieve this musical ecstasy.'

Fritz has tried to re-create this musical ecstasy by rigging up several pieces of gym equipment to a computer so that using the machines produces electronic music. Fritz calls the system jymmin – 'a mixture of jammin', like Bob Marley and gym,' he explains. Fritz uses the system to investigate a phenomenon most of us are familiar with: music eases the pain of working out.

Research has shown that syncing your movements with a beat seems to increase stamina and metabolic efficiency. The mainstream explanation for these effects is that music serves as a distraction. But Fritz's study suggests that's not the whole story.

Fritz asked 61 nonathlete volunteers to work out on one of three machines and then to answer questions about their perceived exertion. For most participants, perceived exertion was lower during the jymmin session than when passively listening to music. That's significant, Fritz says, because when jymmin you can't be distracted – on the contrary, you must focus on your muscles.

Fritz notes that there are many possibilities as to why his set-up would lead to lower perceived exertion. One explanation is what he terms 'musical agency', the sense that you're composing or tweaking the music.

Fritz also plans on studying the social aspects in more depth. Social influence is particularly strong after using the machines for 10 minutes or more, when you really start to feel the burn. 'You reach a point where you think, "Wow, I'm ready to sit down and go home." But you realise someone else is just starting some kind of improvisation and so you think, "OK, OK, I can't stop now,"' he says. 'All of a sudden, your idea that you've reached your limit is totally gone. And you can play on and on and on.' ■

Flower Power
Studies have shown that playing music can help flowers grow faster and be healthier. In one study, plants that were exposed to regular death metal proved more resistant to pests and disease than plants exposed to other types of music.

Research shows that syncing your movements with a beat seems to increase stamina and metabolic efficiency, so how can we use music to improve our workouts?

It's not easy being green: Scientists think that red-eyed tree frogs may use their vibrant colours to startle predators, giving them a chance to leap to safety.

Birthday cake

The practice of giving a cake for a birthday dates far back in Western culture. The ancient Greeks baked round or moon-shaped honey cakes as a tribute to Artemis, a moon goddess. Candles gave the cakes a moonlike glow. The Romans held private celebrations in honour of friends and family. A 50th-birthday cake was made with flour, olive oil, honey and grated cheese.

The modern birthday cake, however, may have begun in medieval Germany, where a *Kinderfeste* was held in celebration of the birthday of a child. Early in the morning, the child was presented with a cake topped by lighted candles. During the day, the candles were kept burning; the cake was eaten after dinner. ■

Curlew Sandpiper

Calidris ferruginea
LENGTH: 19–21 cm (7.5–8.3 in)
WINGSPAN: 44 cm (17.3 in)

In winter, the curlew sandpiper is pale grey and white, but in the summertime, it develops crimson underparts for the breeding season. A gregarious species, it can be found in large flocks, foraging in the soft mud of marshes and coastal areas. Its long legs make for easy wading through mudflats, where you can hear its rippling *chirrup-chirrip-chirrip* call. ■

Roller Coasters

As a chain hauls a roller coaster car to its first and highest peak, the riders sense something in the pit of their stomachs: the car is gaining potential energy. The heavier the loaded car and the higher it goes, the more potential energy it takes on. When the car reaches the top and the stored energy is at its maximum, the chain releases and it falls.

As the car plunges, what it loses in potential energy it gains in kinetic energy – the energy of motion. Pushed upwards once again by the track, the car reverses that transformation, converting motion energy back to the potential energy that comes with elevated position. Indeed, the whole ride can be seen as a thrilling exercise in energy conversion. In theory at least (assuming negligible friction and air resistance), the total mechanical energy of the ride remains constant throughout. Just as the applied force of mechanical lifting invested the system with potential energy at the beginning of the ride, the coaster comes to a stop with the application of brakes – and the final, friction-induced dissipation of motion energy into heat energy. ■

This magic moment of sea foam hitting the beach takes hundreds, sometimes thousands of photos in exactly the right conditions to capture.

IT WAS JUNE, AND THE WORLD SMELLED OF ROSES

JUNE

Scheveningen, The Netherlands

Savour a timeless bash celebrating fresh 'silver from the sea'.

Dutch politicians and celebrities demonstrate proper herring-eating form at an alfresco seaside festival celebrating Hollandse Nieuwe – the first barrel of herrings of the season.

In the 18th century, Dutch fishermen would raise their festive *vlaggetjes* (pennants) when setting out to catch the first herring of the season. While that tradition has faded, every June a crowd gathers in Scheveningen, a beach town near The Hague, to celebrate Vlaggetjesdag (Flag Day). The harbour district quakes with marching bands, craft demonstrations and other traditional events.

On the Thursday before Vlaggetjesdag, the first barrel of Hollandse Nieuwe, or new herring, is auctioned off for charity. The season lasts just six weeks, with the remaining catch frozen to enjoy at a later date. 'Some fishmongers call it nieuwe the entire year,' observes Frank Heyn, owner of Frank's Smokehouse in Amsterdam. 'But a few months after the auction, it has lost its pizzazz.'

At bustling harbour stalls, plump fillets are gobbled down with raw onions and pickles and chased with shots of *korenwijn,* a Dutch gin. The proper technique? Hold the herring aloft by the tail and bite upwards. ■

Masters of Holding Their Breath

Over millions of years, diving mammals developed the ability to slow their heart rate and stop their breathing when starting a dive. Champion divers such as elephant seals can hold their breath for as much as two hours. Many of these diving mammals have specialised oxygen-binding proteins that give them a larger store of oxygen while underwater.

How Spices Tickle Your Lips

What's the difference between a spicy meal and being tickled? Not much, from your lips' perspective. A study has shown that Szechuan pepper activates the same nerves that respond to a light physical touch.

Scientists investigating psychophysics – the relationship between physical reality and what we perceive – have discovered that the tickle caused by a feather is similar to that of spicy pepper.

Researchers at the University College London Institute of Cognitive Neuroscience found that people experienced the same sensation when either hot pepper or a light touch was placed on their lips. The study delves into the field of psychophysics, which 'describes the relation between physical reality and what we actually perceive,' in the words of its lead author, Nobuhiro Hagura.

For the study, they neeeded some brave volunteers. Participants were asked to describe what they felt when a solution of ground Szechuan pepper was applied to their lips. 'Tingling' was the most common adjective.

Next, they placed one finger on a machine and compared various vibrations to the tingling on their lips. People reported that these sensations were similar when the machine ran at a frequency of 50 hertz. When researchers placed the machine against the participants' lips, sure enough, it felt just like the Szechuan pepper. This suggested that the tingling sensation was linked to the light touch nerve fibres.

For the final phase of the study, they placed the machine against the volunteers' lips for a longer period to desensitise the nerves. Then they applied the pepper, predicting that if it were really activated by the same fibres it would seem less spicy. 'That's exactly what we found,' Hagura says. 'Thus, the Szechuan pepper and physical touch sensation share the same pathway to the brain.' ■

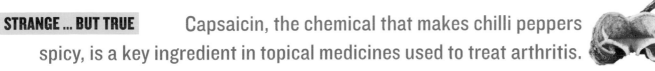

STRANGE … BUT TRUE Capsaicin, the chemical that makes chilli peppers spicy, is a key ingredient in topical medicines used to treat arthritis.

VISIONS OF EARTH

Members of the cult of Maria Lionza use candles to summon the spirit as part of a cleansing ritual called Velación, during believers' annual pilgrimage to Venezuela's Cerro de Sorte.

Eight Popular Delica- cies of the Insect Kind

Stink bugs have an apple flavour and red agave worms are spicy. A bite of tree worm apparently brings pork crackling to mind.

There are more than 1,900 edible insect species on Earth, hundreds of which are already part of the diet in many countries. Many insects are packed with protein, fibre, good fats and vital minerals – as much or more than many other food sources. This information will come in handy for following the latest recommendation from the United Nations: consume more insects.

If you're looking to incorporate some creepy crawlies into your diet, here's where to start:

Grasshoppers, Crickets and Locusts Grasshoppers and their ilk are the most consumed type of insect, probably because they're all over the place. There are a lot of different kinds and they're a great protein source. Hoppers have a neutral flavour, so they pick up other flavours nicely. Cricket curry, anyone?

Bees and Wasps We love bees for their honey, but they have more to give. Bee brood (bees in egg or larval form) taste like peanuts or almonds, while wasps have a pine-nutty flavour.

Ants You're probably thinking that it takes a lot of ants to make a meal. True, but they pack a punch: 100 grams (35 oz) of red ant provides some 14 grams of protein (more than eggs), nearly 48 grams of calcium and lots of iron, among other nutrients. And all in less than 100 calories.

Stink bugs If you can get past the smell, these insects apparently add an apple flavour to sauces and are a valuable source of iodine. They're also known to have anaesthetic and analgesic properties. Who would have thought?

Beetles In the Amazon basin, parts of Africa and other heavily forested regions, people munch on a diverse array of beetles. Beetles have more protein than most other insects. Native Americans would roast them over coals and eat them like popcorn. ∎

Our Ancient Diet
Cave paintings in northern Spain show people collecting wild bee nests – both the honey and the protein inside could have been an important part of our early human ancestors' diet.

Pig Olympians

At the Pig Olympics in Russia, the pigs might not be flying, but they do show their athletic prowess.

Since 2003, specially bred and trained piglets have been taking part in the Pig Olympics, organised by the Sport-Pig Federation. Young pigs from several countries take part in the games, which include pig racing, pig swimming and pigball. Former contestants have included Mykola from Ukraine, Nelson from South Africa and the home favourite, Kostik Russisch Schwein.

In the running race, pigs have to be encouraged by their coaches, who run behind them to keep them on course and make them run faster. In pig swimming, which was introduced in 2006, competitors attempt to paddle to the other end of a small pool. However, the pigs are often more interested in bumping into each other than racing and piglets tend to get stuck in the lane lines. Pigball, a game not unlike football, involves piglets split into two teams chasing a ball covered in fish oil towards goals in each corner of a pen.

Alexei Sharshkov, vice president of the Sport-Pig Federation, which has around a hundred members, says the pigs do not end up on anyone's dinner table. "They go on to produce a new generation of sport pigs. They don't get eaten," he says 'How could you eat a competitor who is known around the world?'

Moscow, Russia: A piglet expertly balances a ball on its snout during the pigball event at Pig Olympics. The four-legged athletes also compete in running and swimming events.

How To: Get Water From a Cactus

Nothing's more important to survival than water. This is one way to find some in a desert.

1 Identify a barrel cactus: these are spiny, cylindrical, short cacti with pink or yellow flowers. Cut off the top of the cactus with a knife, avoiding contact with the spiky outer skin.

2 Mash the insides with a stick or spoon until reduced to a pulp.

3 Strain the pulp through a thin cloth, like a bandana, catching liquid In your mouth or a cup. It may have an unpleasant taste. If you don't have a cloth, chew the pulp for the liquid, but don't eat the pulp.

EXPERT TIP: Drink plenty of fluids even if you do not feel thirsty. Injury and death can occur from dehydration, which can happen quickly and may go unnoticed.

Man's Best Friend: Dogs and Humans Evolved Together

The bond between dogs and humans is ancient and enduring.

Dogs snuggle up to us at night, gambol by our side during daily walks and flop adoringly at our feet at night. Now science has found that several groups of genes in humans and dogs – including those related to diet, neurological processes and disease – have been evolving in parallel for millennia.

'As domestication is often associated with large increases in population density and crowded living conditions, these "unfavorable" environments might be the selective pressure that drove the rewiring of both species,' the authors of a recent study surmise.

For example, crowded conditions may have conferred an advantage on less aggressive dogs, leading to more submissive canines and eventually to the pets whose puppy-dog eyes gaze at us with unconditional affection.

The scientists involved in the study sequenced the genomes of four grey wolves from Russia and China, three Chinese street dogs and three domesticated breeds – a German shepherd, a Belgian malinois and a Tibetan mastiff. They were then able to figure out which genes were associated with domestication and how far back that shift may have occurred.

The team also looked at the dog genes selected for during domestication and compared them with human genes. 'The history of dog domestication is often depicted as a two-stage process,' wrote Weiwei Zhai, a study co-author. 'The first stage is from wolves to dogs. The second stage is from dogs to breeds.'

Southeast Asia's street dogs may be an evolutionary bridge between wolves and purebred dogs due to their greater genetic diversity when compared with other street dogs from around the world, Zhai explained. This would make the Chinese street dogs a kind of 'missing link' among canines.

When they compared canine sequences with the human genome, the team found that sequences for things such as the transport of neurotransmitters like serotonin, cholesterol processing and cancer have been selected for in both humans and dogs.

It's hard to know whether the parallel evolution in the genomes of humans and dogs is unique or not without further comparisons between humans and other domestic animals such as goats or horses. Even so, the study adds another chapter to the story of dog domestication – a story far from over. ■

The Purrfect Match
Cats were probably domesticated more recently than dogs. Like their wild relatives, domestic cats have rough tongues that are meant to clean every last morsel from an animal bone (it's also helpful for grooming themselves).

Man's best friend has been evolving alongside us, adapting to humans' changing conditions for thousands of years, a new study has found.

A tiny island appears from the mist on lake near Prince George, British Columbia's biggest and most northerly city.

Swimming Pools

The great ancestor of swimming pools is the Great Bath at Mohenjo Daro in what is now Pakistan. The bath dates back to 3000 B.C. and was about 12 metres (40 ft) by  8 metres (26 ft), sealed with tar. The ancient Sinhalese had far more elaborate pools known as the Kuttam Pokuna, built in the fourth century B.C., which used a filtering system.

Ancient Greeks and Romans built swimming pools for athletics and for military training. The first heated pool was also a Roman innovation, built by the wealthy Gaius Maecenas in the first century B.C.

For hundreds of years, swimming pools remained rare, but they gained popularity in the mid-19th century after six indoor pools with diving boards were built in London in 1837. ■

Whitethroat

Sylvia communis
LENGTH: 13–15 cm (5–6 in)
WINGSPAN: 21 cm (8.3 in)

The *wed-wed* call of the common whitethroat can be heard as flocks pass through in the summer and autumn, before heading to Africa for the winter. Subsisting on a diet of insects, berries and fruit, it flicks a long tail as it moves quickly in and out of cover. The whitethroat sings a beautiful song from the early morning until dusk and can be found nesting in bushes and shrubs. It prefers to avoid mountainous or urban areas. ■

Hovercraft

Perhaps the most famous hovercraft ever built were those that – until 2000, when the Channel Tunnel opened – carried passengers across the English Channel in a half hour. But they're also used in disaster relief, some rescue and military operations and, of course, for recreation – what could be more fun than zipping around on a cushion of air?

The ultimate all-terrain vehicles, hovercraft can move over slippery, boggy, or bumpy land, not to mention over water. The craft creates lift with a powerful fan that forces air underneath it. This pressurised air is mostly contained within a flexible skirt, which allows the vehicle to travel damage-free over small obstructions. Most hovercraft have a propeller at the rear to create thrust, propelling the vehicle forward as they push air back. Rudders mounted at the fan's outlet direct the flow of this air. By manipulating the angle of the rudders, the pilot is able to control the craft's direction. Some large crafts use multiple engines to carry particularly heavy loads.

Like the wheel before it, the hovercraft makes travel faster and easier by minimising surface friction. ■

Weston-Super-Mare, UK: Riders in the RHL Weston beach race tackle a course complete with man-made jumps and sand dunes in a three-hour test of endurance.

'TIS SUMMER'S VERY BREATH / THAT GENTLY SHAKES THE RUSTLING TREES

JULY

Mount Fuji, Japan
Catch a sunrise on the sacred mountain.

Mount Fuji, Japan: One of the world's most recognisable mountains, Mount Fuji is surrounded by five lakes, including Lake Kawaguchiko, the second largest.

The Japanese have a saying: 'A wise man climbs Fuji-san once, but only a fool climbs it twice.' Ascending the world's most iconic volcano and watching the sun rise over Tokyo and across the Japanese Alps is indeed a once-in-a-lifetime experience – ideally undertaken during the July-to-August climbing season.

At 3,776 metres (12,388 ft), Mount Fuji is Japan's highest mountain, yet you'll find many novice hikers heading for the top. For the religious, climbing Fuji-san is the chance to commune with Amaterasu, the celestial sun goddess from whom the Japanese imperial family claims direct descent. But most make the trek to watch the sun rise over Tokyo's never-ending metropolis. When the golden moment arrives, you'll hear a collective shout of 'Banzai! – Hurrah!' Enjoy the sweep of the clouds and glittering lakes far below. Then descend by the Gotemba-guchi trail and race through soft volcanic sand. After climbing Fuji-san, you will actually feel like you're walking on air. ▪

Local Language

A survey of hundreds of languages showed that languages spoken at high altitudes are more likely to contain a certain kind of sound made using short bursts of air, called ejective consonants, according to the study. These sounds, not found in the English language, may be easier to produce in areas of low air pressure, as it takes less effort to compress the air.

How Old Is That Lion?
A Guide to Aging Animals

Panthera leo
WEIGHT: 120–190 kg
(265–420 lb)
RANGE: Throughout
Africa and in the Gir
Forest in India

Big cats may not have birth certificates, but they do display telltale signs of aging. By taking a closer look at its hair, muscle tone and behaviour, researchers can figure out how old a lion is.

Lions in Serengeti National Park. Duller fur and a more visible bone structure can be clues to a lion's advancing age.

To figure out how old a tree is, look at its rings. To figure out how old a cat is, you want to start out with the hair, says Tammy Schmidt, curator of carnivores and ungulates at the Philadelphia Zoo. 'Hair gets dry and brittle and grey as it ages,' she explains. 'That's true for everything from house cats to big cats like an elderly lion or tiger.'

Of course, you don't want to get too close to even an elderly lion or tiger. But it is possible to see changes in their fur coats from a distance. 'The hair becomes duller,' Schmidt continues. 'A cat is going to take less care and time with their fur coat [as it ages].'

There are other clues, but they may be harder to see. 'A carnivore like a lion or tiger is made to be secret and sly about what's happening to them,' says Schmidt. 'You need to put all of the pieces of the puzzle together.'

Those pieces include things like muscle tone – animals become less toned as they age – and how the tail fits between an animal's hips. 'You look at how full the rump is,' she says. 'Can you see ribs? You look at how they're moving. Older animals are going to have more pronounced stepping because their eyesight is diminishing.' ■

To figure out a fish's age, look in its ear. Its tiny ear bones have annual growth rings (like a tree) that tell you its age.

Like a spaceship ready to lift off, a whirling carnival ride throws off orbs of light in this panoramic time exposure, taken at the Minnesota State Fair, USA.

Cockroaches Dined on Dinosaur Dung

These ancient insects had the messy job of cleaning up what the giant reptiles left behind.

We all know dinosaurs didn't enjoy the luxury of modern plumbing and there were no sewage tanks back then. The job of keeping the landscape tidy was left to a much smaller worker: the cockroach – more specifically, cockroaches from the now extinct *Blattulidae* family.

Peter Vršanský of the Geological Institute at the Slovak Academy of Sciences in Bratislava, Slovakia, figured this out almost by mistake. When he started his study, he was researching the diet of the ancient *Blattulidae* cockroaches and he expected it to resemble the diets of other cockroaches from the period. None of the others dined on dinosaur dung, so it wasn't even on the research team's radar.

But then they cracked open a fossilised cockroach that had been discovered in an amber deposit from Lebanon and created a virtual 3-D version of the cockroach to study instead of picking apart the original. They were surprised to find large wood particles in the cockroach's gut. The particles had smooth edges, indicating that the cockroach had not munched on them.

So, who ate those wood particles first? Dinosaurs!

During the Mesozoic period, cockroaches were the most common insect in most areas. Modern cleaner-uppers like dung beetles and flies weren't around during the Triassic or most of the Jurassic periods, which cover about half of the span of the dinosaur era.

The *Blattulidae* cockroaches were not like the modern, wood-eating cockroaches and termites that we deal with today. But the link between dino poo and cockroaches didn't die with the dinosaurs or with the *Blattulidae* family – several modern cockroaches feast on the faeces of birds, known dinosaur descendants. It looks like some habits are hard to break. ■

The Scoop on Ancient Poop
Fossilised faeces, known as coprolites, tells us a lot about early animals. A 240-million-year-old fossil revealed that some of the earliest dinosaurs used communal latrines.

Bailey Jr the buffalo relaxing at home with his owner Jim Sautner Jim has had his car modified so that Bailey can also join him on trips.

Bailey the Bison
One Big Best Friend

Jim Sautner, who lives in Canada's Alberta province, keeps a bison named Bailey Junior as a pet. After Bailey's mother died, Sautner and his wife Linda took him in, feeding him with a bottle until he was old enough to eat solid food. Bailey Junior is actually Sautner's second bison pet. Bailey Senior died in 2008.

Sautner says that caring for a bison isn't much trouble. He eats buckets of hay and oats and takes care of his own coat. Since the buffalo doesn't require much grooming, all Sautner has to do is take an air hose from the garage to clean Bailey up for a parade or function – of which he participates in many. Bailey Junior is something of a celebrity in the area.

Sautner says that in his old house, Bailey would come in and watch TV, drink water out of the sink and generally behave like a dog. After Sautner and his wife moved, however, Bailey was not allowed inside. But he is allowed in the car – Sautner removed the roof and passenger seats and reinforced the floorboards so that Bailey could ride around town with him and their cocker spaniel, Charlie Brown. 'He's my best friend,' says Sautner. 'He's my buffalo.'

How To: Fight Off a Shark
If you find yourself face to face with a shark, remember these tips.

1. If you face an aggressive shark while floating unprotected, slap the surface of the water with cupped hands to make a series of loud bangs, or shout underwater.

2. Kick the shark in the head or snout.

3. In a group of people, form a tight circle facing outward and kick or strike the shark with hard objects.

4. If the shark bites down, do not play dead. Hit its most sensitive areas: the eyes and gills.

EXPERT TIP: In general, dangerous sharks have wide mouths and visible teeth, while relatively harmless sharks have small mouths on the underside of their heads.

Inca Child Sacrifice Victims Were Drugged

Mummy hair reveals that young victims found near the summit of Volcán Llullaillaco in Argentina used coca and alcohol before their ceremonial death.

Three Inca mummies found on a mountain in Argentina were so well preserved that they put a human face on the ancient ritual of *capacocha* – which ended with their sacrifice. The bodies of the 13-year-old Llullaillaco Maiden and her younger companions have revealed that mind-altering substances played a part in their deaths and during the ceremonial processes that prepared them for their final hours.

Under biochemical analysis, the Maiden's hair yielded a record of what she ate and drank during the last two years of her life. This evidence seems to support historical accounts of a few selected children taking part in a year of sacred ceremonies that would ultimately lead to their sacrifice. In Inca religious ideology, coca and alcohol could induce altered states associated with the sacred. But the substances likely played a more pragmatic role as well, disorienting and sedating the young victims on the high mountainside to make them more accepting of their own grim fates.

Because hair grows about a centimetre (0.4 in) a month and remains unchanged thereafter, the Maiden's long braids contain a time line of markers that record her diet, including consumption of substances like coca and alcohol in the form of chicha, a fermented brew made from maize. It is their incredible preservation that made possible the kinds of technical analysis that allowed experts to re-create the events that took place some 500 years ago.

The markers show that she appears to have been selected for sacrifice a year before her actual death. During this period, her life changed dramatically, as did her consumption of both coca and alcohol, which were then controlled substances not available for everyday use.

On the day of the Maiden's death, the drugs may have made her more docile, putting her in a stupor or perhaps even rendering her unconscious. That theory seems to be supported by her relaxed, seated position inside the tomblike structure, and the fact that the artefacts around her were undisturbed, including the feathered headdress she wore as she drifted off to death. Chewed coca leaves were found in the mummy's mouth upon her discovery in 1999. ■

Feeling Sick? The coca plant is grown on the slopes of the Andes. Making a tea or simply chewing on the leaves can prevent altitude sickness and even treat bone fractures, due to its high levels of calcium.

Tests reveal that this sacrificed
13-year-old took quantities of
coca the last year of her life, but
her alcohol use surged only in
her final weeks.

Double bubble: Some children enjoy some simple fun in their back garden courtesy of a bubble machine.

Sandwiches

John Montagu, the fourth Earl of Sandwich, certainly contributed his title to the popular snack of two pieces of bread holding some type of filling. In 1762, Montagu, an avid gambler, realised the type of food would allow him to eat while at the card table. However, the snack itself dates back to the first century B.C.

Jewish sage Hillel the Elder placed lamb and bitter herbs between two pieces of matzo bread during Passover; the Romans called this concoction *cibus Hilleli*, 'Hillel's snack'. Other cultures, including Middle and Near Eastern, made sandwiches long before they caught on in the West, and in Europe it seems the Dutch *belegde broodje* ('filled roll') was popular a century before the Earl of Sandwich ever saw a cribbage board. ■

Bee-eater

Merops apiaster

LENGTH: 25–29 cm (10.0–11.5 in)
WINGSPAN: 44–49 cm (17–19 in)

As its name suggests, this richly coloured bird eats mainly insects, particularly bees, wasps and hornets. Bee-eaters nest in colonies on sandy riverbanks, where their distinctive pleasant trill can be heard. The European Bee-eater breeds in parts of southern and northwestern Europe and winters in more tropical regions of Africa, India, and Sri Lanka. ■

Fireworks

A fireworks display is an explosion designed for maximum visual impact. Before the *oohs* and *ahhs*, however, the first challenge is to get a packet of chemical reactants into the sky. This is usually accomplished with simple gunpowder, lit by a fuse. The gunpowder is packed so that the resultant expanding gases are forced to escape rearward. This propels the shell upwards until the fuse burns into what's called the burst charge at its core. The burst-charge chemicals explode, lighting and casting in all directions hundreds of 'stars', small packages of reactants selected to create colour. Different shells produce the variety of shapes and effects.

The reactants are metallic salts: lithium or strontium produces red; barium nitrates make green; copper compounds result in blue; sodium creates yellow; charcoal and steel produce sparkling gold; and titanium makes white.

The chemicals undergo a fast and violent reaction; bonds among molecules of the solid chemicals break apart, yielding hot, concentrated gases that spread out in a flash, transforming energy into sound, movement and coloured light. ■

Cable Beach, Australia: Renowned as one of the world's most stunning beaches, Cable Beach is named after the telegraph cable that was laid between Broome and Java in 1889.

OH, THE SUMMER NIGHT / HAS A SMILE OF LIGHT / AND SHE SITS ON A SAPPHIRE THRONE

AUGUST

Tahiti, French Polynesia

Bask in the sun where ancient and modern traditions collide.

Female fire dancers light up the night in this dramatic display in Tahiti, French Polynesia. Tahiti's dance festival, Heiva I Tahiti, takes place every July.

Spend a night at Tahiti's summer dance festival, Heiva I Tahiti. It's a three-week homage to the sensual that unfolds on an open-air stage in Papeete, the territorial capital. Festivalgoers will arrive during the island's most pleasant month, July, when it's possible to explore Tahiti's blue lagoons and cloud-shrouded peaks by day in temperatures that hover in the upper 20s Celsius (low 80s Fahrenheit).

After dark, the real fun starts. It's time for an expressly Tahitian display of music and movement: quivering hips and hands, at a pace that makes hula seem slow motion and a primal drumbeat that works its way into your soul and stays there long after the music has stopped.

Renowned dancer Tumata Robinson calls the festival a 'voyage of discovery' through nearly 2,000 years of Tahitian culture. Hollywood's 1935 *Mutiny on the Bounty* helped spark the dance revival, but unlike the movie, the festival allows visitors to do more than watch: feel free to offer a hand with rehearsals or making costumes before the shows. ■

Long-Held Myth About Cheetahs Busted

Like a fine sports car, cheetahs are born to run and for many years, researchers believed the animals' blazing speed came at a cost: the danger of overheating on a hunt. A recent study, however, hypothesised that the cats' post-hunt temperature rise is due to a stress response in cheetahs on the lookout for other predators or even tourists.

Honk if You Think Geese Make Good Guards

Anser cygnoides
WINGSPAN: 160–185 cm (5.2–6.1 ft)
WEIGHT: 2.8–3.5 kg (6.2–7.7 lb)

Police in rural parts of China's Xinjiang Province are no longer turning to dogs to stand guard at police stations at night. They're using geese instead.

Noisy and territorial, with excellent eyesight and hearing, geese make great guards – as this photographer found out when he tried to take their picture!

According to a recent report, a man tried to break into a police station to take back a motorbike confiscated by the police. The guard geese sounded the alarm, awakening the sleeping officers. But, really? Guard geese?

Patrick Cumins, director of bird conservation at Audubon Connecticut, has seen barnyard geese in action and has lots of insights into goose behaviour. 'They have amazing hearing,' Cumins says. 'And almost all birds have amazing eyesight. Not only do they see better at a distance than humans do, they can also see things up close [better than we do].'

Birds have a much wider range of wavelengths they can view. Our eyes have three different colour sensors that combine to build the picture in our brain. Birds add a fourth: ultraviolet, making things look much sharper. They can pick out smaller objects as well as smaller movements. And when they spot an intruder? 'In terms of alerting people to activity, yeah, they're very vigilant,' remarks Cumins. 'They're territorial. And certain species can be quite loud.'

Plus, they're harder to distract than dogs. 'Dogs, you can give some steak and they might be a little distracted. It's pretty hard to give geese something that's going to distract them enough where they wouldn't make noise,' says Cumins. ■

STRANGE ... BUT TRUE Snakes have been used as guard animals throughout the world. In London, for instance, a cobra was used to keep an enormous sapphire safe.

Taking a load off: Doyok the orangutan passes some time on a convenient bench in Tanjung Putting National Park, Borneo, Indonesia.

The Other Golden Rule

Most mammals take the same amount of time (about 20 seconds) to take care of business.

Like many new parents, David Hu, a mechanical engineer, has changed a lot of nappies. Unlike many new parents, however, these soggy nappies caused Hu to think about the physics of urination. 'While I was changing these diapers, I was wondering how it would be different for different animals,' Hu says. 'How much fluid would they create and how long would it take to leave the body?' It might sound silly, but urination is serious business in the medical and veterinary worlds.

Hu wanted to know how urination varied between species. Enter the pee cam. Using high-speed cameras, Hu's team recorded peeing animals and measured the amount of urine produced. They obtained measurements of the animals' bladder and urethra from other researchers.

Hu suspected that bigger animals would take longer, since they had to expel larger volumes of urine. The bladder of a large domestic dog can hold 1.4 litres (a third of a gallon) of fluid, while an elephant's bladder can hold 160 litres (42 gal) – enough to fill three large rubbish bins. But when they began determining the urination duration of each of these animal species, they found otherwise. 'Even though you have thousands of times more urine, it's coming out in the same amount of time, which is around 20 seconds,' reports Hu.

Urinary tract measurements helped to solve the mystery of how animals of such different sizes all pee for the same amount of time. Larger animals not only had larger bladders, they also had longer and wider urethras. The length of the urethra increases the force of gravity on the urine, which in turn increases how fast pee flows out of the body. These increases correlate with the increase in body mass, so that an elephant can empty its bladder in the same amount of time as a cat. ■

Be Kind and Flush Those 20 seconds really add up over time – according to a number of studies, the average person spends about three years of their life on the toilet.

Albert Einstein the Goldfish

When it comes to this fish's intelligence, it's all relative.

He may not qualify for the World Cup, but Albert Einstein the calico fantail goldfish sure can handle a football. To train his fish to push the ball into a goal, owner Dean Pomerleau held a straw under the water and dropped food pellets through it. Eventually, the fish associated the straw's tip with food.

Then Pomerleau placed a weighted-down miniature football and goal in Albert's tank and lured Albert to the ball with a straw. The fish would get treats when he touched the ball. Soon, Albert was guiding it into the net all by himself.

'Now when I put the ball and goal into the tank, he instantly swims up to the ball and starts pushing it in,' Pomerleau says. Al doesn't need shinpads – but maybe he could use some finpads!

And football isn't Albert's only talent – he has a repertoire of six tricks, including doing the limbo and swimming through hoops

Theoretical physics might be a bit of a stretch but Albert Einstein the goldfish is a brilliant footballer. Or should that be finballer?

and tunnels. Pomerleau and his son, Kyle, have started a 'fish school' from their home in Pennsylvania, where they train goldfish, betta fish, parrot chiclids and others. The Pomerleaus' betta fish (also named after a famous intellectual, Isaac Newton) learned how to swim through hoops on command in just two weeks. ◾

How To: Make a Fishing Hook and Line

Fish are relatively easy to catch and a good source of protein.

1 Find a small, thin piece of bone, turtle shell, or wood, sharp enough to use as a hook. Tie a piece of string, dental floss or twine to the middle of it.

2 Turn the hook parallel to the string and bait it with a worm or grub. Make sure the bait covers the entire hook.

3 Tie the other end of the twine to a long stick to use as a fishing rod. Throw the baited hook into water; when the bait sinks to the bottom pull the twine back and recast.

4 When a fish swallows the bait, the sharp object will be lodged inside and you can pull it in.

EXPERT TIP: The best place to forage is on the banks and streams of rivers. There are almost an unlimited number of edible plants to choose. Unless you can identify these plants, it's safer to start with palms, bamboos and common fruits.

The Physics of Waterslides

Put on your bathing suit. It's about to be a wet – and bumpy – ride as we dive into the science of your summer holiday.

At the top of Walt Disney World's Summit Plummet waterslide – which stands 37 metres (120 ft) above the ground – thrill seekers have been known to turn back. It's not hard to see why: the 12-storey waterslide has one of the tallest and fastest drops in the world. Riders reach speeds of up to 90 kilometres an hour (60 mph) as they plummet down the free-fall slide with fake snow banks on either side.

You can think of a waterslide like a roller coaster – only wet and with no safety belt. Gravity gets riders from the top to the bottom. 'You start out at the top of the slide at rest,' explains Eric Martell, an associate professor of physics and astronomy at Millikin University, 'and then you have some forces acting on you which cause you to accelerate.'

Several forces act on riders on a waterslide: gravity, of course, but also the friction between your body and the slide and how the water interacts with the slide itself. 'Water acts as a lubricant between you and the slide,' Martell says, 'but it also pushes you along like a river. And everything that happens to you on a waterslide, it's because of the forces of gravity and friction.'

On a serpentine slide – one that whips riders back and forth along curves – there's something else to keep in mind: inertia, or resistance to changing speed. Each time you reach a curve on a serpentine slide, your body tries to keep going forward. But if it did, you'd plunge over the edge of the slide. 'That's why the waterslide has curved sides,' says Martell. 'Your inertia is trying to take you through the waterslide and out. But instead, you go up the sides of the slides.'

Rick Hunter, president and CEO of ProSlide Technology, has tested every kind of waterslide curve – from large loops to tight corners – and how the human body reacts to each one. 'You want to start out with a bigger curve, because a curve with a longer radius is a smoother ride,' he says. 'Safety is our number one concern. We're thinking about things like, Are you going to stay on the fibreglass tube?' Hunter adds, 'It's really easy to do a computer model and look at curves and drops and forecast rider position and speed.' According to Hunter, the best slides have a combination of elements. But one in particular should be in every slide: 'We're always looking for the big splash.' ■

Time for a Dip The swim rings that you float around a pool or lake on in the summer were originally designed as the inner tubes of older car tyres. They are also often used for sledding, rafting and other recreational activities.

The science of waterslides: Gravity works against the friction caused between you and the slide, while the water pushes you along and acts as a lubricant.

A performer illuminates colourful graffiti by spinning lit wire wool. Long exposure photography captures the glowing trails created by flying sparks.

Air-Conditioning

What did we do before we had air-conditioning? Buildings were constructed differently, for one thing. Homes had porches, high ceilings and wide eaves under the roofs that allowed hot air to rise away from the lower floors. Before that, some buildings had water circulating through walls (ancient Romans), water-powered fan wheels (China), cisterns and wind towers (Persia), or ventilators (medieval Egypt).

Modern air-conditioning was made possible by British scientist Michael Faraday's 1820 discovery that compressed, liquefied ammonia could chill the air around it as it evaporated. The term 'air-conditioning' was coined in 1906 by American textile manufacturer Stuart W. Cramer. ■

Swallow

Hirundo rustica
LENGTH: 17–21 cm (6.7–8.3 in)
WINGSPAN: 28–30 cm (11–12 in)

An exuberant flyer, swallows are often seen in small flocks skimming low over the surface of a field or pond, taking insects in midair. Lowlands and foothills near open water are home for the swallow during breeding season. It repeats a high-pitched, slightly squeaky *chee-jit* call in flight and sings a warbling song when still. The swallow has a wide range, and flies as far south as Africa, Australia and Argentina to winter. ■

Thunderstorms

Thunderstorms start most often on a spring or summer day with warm, moist air. This warm air rises above cooler air, sometimes nudged upward by a sea breeze or cold front. As the warm air rises, its water vapour condenses to form clouds. The condensing gas gives up heat, which warms surrounding air. This warm air in turn pushes farther upwards.

As the atmosphere becomes less stable, vertical motion increases. The cloud gets taller until it forms a thunderhead, whose mushroom-like shape can be seen from a distance. Meanwhile, warm updraughts continue to lift small droplets to great heights into colder air.

Amid this turbulence, water particles collide, knocking negatively charged electrons from rising particles. The extra electrons give the bottom of the cloud a negative charge, while the top is positively charged. That's how an electrical field forms within the storm. Zap! Lightning suddenly heats the air to more than 28,000 degrees Celsius (50,000°F) in less than a second. This causes air to expand explosively, violently compacting the air around it – a disturbance called a shock wave that our ears hear as thunder. ■

Creating order out of chaos:
Skydivers come together
in midair, holding onto each
other's limbs, or 'grippers' on
their suits, before breaking apart
and releasing their parachutes.

SEP

SILVER-MISTY MORNING, / JEWELLED COBWEBS SPARKLING

TEMBER

The Masurian Lakes, Poland
Catch the autumn foliage reflected in crystalline waters.

A foggy autumn day in Poland's Masurian Lakes region. After the end of the summer holidays when the leaves change colour is the perfect time for a visit.

The secret has long been out about Poland's Masurian Lakes region in summer, but the area makes a splendid autumn retreat as well. By late August, holidays have ended for summer revellers and a new season beckons with its open waters and changing shoreline scenery. Senses are heightened by the air's slight chill. But the days – especially in September – are warm enough for a comfortable afternoon out on the seemingly endless panorama of lakes – some two thousand to choose from. And by mid-month, the lakeshores' palette begins to turn fiery red and orange, shimmering in the crystal-clear water.

The Masurian chain of lakes, some interlinked by canals, starts 240 kilometres (150 mi) northeast of Warsaw and stretches nearly to the Kaliningrad (Russia) and Lithuanian borders. As well as boating, get the blood flowing by hiking the leaf-strewn trails of the Masurian Landscape Park, a forest and biosphere that surrounds the waters. ■

Volcanoes 'Scream' Before They Erupt

The small earthquakes that foreshadow some volcanic explosions produce an audible hum that stops just before an eruption. Scientists think this happens as magma is forced through a narrow opening under great pressure into the heart of the mountain. When the rocks shift due to this pressure, earthquakes and a loud noise result.

This Mouse Can Turn Scorpion Venom Into a Painkiller

There's a new contender for the toughest mammal: the southern grasshopper mouse. This little creature attacks and eats bark scorpions.

Onychomys torridus
WEIGHT: 20–40 g
(0.7–1.4 oz)
RANGE: Mexico and southwestern United States

This Arizona bark scorpion has a vicious sting. But the southern grasshopper mouse doesn't care, it's armed with a protein that stops feeling the pain.

The sting of the bark scorpion has been described as having a cigarette stubbed out on your skin, followed by hours of throbbing. The toxins are easily powerful enough to kill most small rodents. But the grasshopper mouse doesn't care. It viciously attacks and eats scorpions. And when it gets stung – and it gets stung a lot – it barely seems to notice. Ashlee Rowe from Michigan State University has discovered how it copes.

The mouse is armed with a protein that stops its nerves from firing whenever it recognises the toxins in a bark scorpion's venom. This prevents the venom from triggering intense pain. In a way, it means that the scorpion's venom actually prevents pain! The southern grasshopper mouse turns a scorpion's sting from a painful killer into a painkiller.

But what about the scorpions? Surely they will eventually evolve a way around the mouse's impunity. Rowe suspects that this might be happening. 'I've begun to look at population differences in the scorpions,' she says. 'There are some populations that are a little more toxic than others and they tend to be the ones that coexist with the grasshopper mouse. I haven't looked at pain levels yet, but there might be some sort of arms race.' ■

STRANGE ... BUT TRUE

Some species of scorpion emit a fluorescent glow when under ultraviolet light.

Suited and booted: These young fashionistas proudly parade their haute couture through the Matonge neighbourhood of Kinshasa, Democratic Republic of Congo.

Growing Teeth and Other Odd Uses for Urine

For those who've lost their teeth to accidents and decay, there may be a new way to restore your pearly whites: urine.

Scientists in China have successfully used cells found in human urine to regrow teeth. If that doesn't have enough of a 'yuck' factor, the scientists grew the teeth in mouse kidneys. The researchers converted cells collected from urine into what's called pluripotent stem cells, which can become any kind of cell in the body. These stem cells were then mixed with dental tissue and implanted into mouse kidneys. The entire process took just a few weeks – several days to incubate the stem cells and then three weeks to grow them in the kidneys, according to the study. Of course, these were not normal teeth; they were soft and misshapen and not actually, you know, attached to a person's jaw.

Though human urine hasn't overtaken the denture industry, other researchers have come up with some surprising and creative ways to reuse the litres of liquid gold each of us create every day.

Urine as Fuel. At the 2012 Maker Faire for innovators in Lagos, Nigeria, a group of three schoolgirls created a backup generator that could run on human urine. The device uses an electrolytic cell to break down the molecules in urine and extract pure hydrogen. One litre (34 oz) of urine can produce up to six hours of electricity.

Urine as Compost. When researchers combined compost with human urine, they found they had created a fertiliser that is superior to compost alone. The trick appears to be the extra nitrogen from the urine, which helps to boost plants' growth.

Urine as Water. NASA has developed a new filtration system to turn human wastewater like sweat and urine into safe drinking water. The Forward Osmosis Bag (FOB) was designed to give astronauts an extra source of water in space. ■

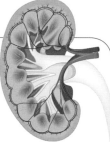

Kidney Power
One kidney is capable of handling the task of filtering the blood and making urine and, if the other is removed, can increase in size by up to 50 percent to take over the whole job.

Rico the Dog
One Brainy Border Collie

Rico is an old dog learning new tricks. This border collie who lives in Dortmund, Germany, understands more than 250 words.

Experts think the average pet dog can understand about 20 commands. But Rico can fetch any of his 260 toys as well as follow dozens of commands. But what really excites scientists is that Rico can learn new words without the repetitive training that most dogs need.

For instance, Rico's owner can place an unfamiliar baseball among seven familiar toys and then say 'Get me the baseball.' Though Rico has never connected the word 'baseball' with the new toy, he retrieves it anyway. Why? Because Rico knows the names of the seven other toys, so he understands that the new toy, the baseball, is the one his owner wants.

Rico has been learning words since he was a puppy. At 10 months old, his owner, Susanne Baus, would tell Rico to retrieve specific toys. He soon developed an extensive vocabulary.

Until Rico, many scientists thought that only humans could learn through the process of elimination. They are now looking for other dogs with Rico's level of intelligence. ■

Clever border collie Rico can recognise and fetch at least 200 objects by name. Is Rico proof that dogs can understand human language?

How To: Splint a Broken Leg

If you suspect a limb is broken and need to move, a splint will keep the injury from worsening.

1 If you cannot put pressure on or move a limb and suspect it is broken – and you can't reach medical help – you may need to make a splint. Find two rigid objects long enough to immobilise the joints above and below the injury. Place them on either side of the limb.

2 Insert padding between the injury and the splint.

3 Secure the splint by tying it in place. Bind it tight enough to support the injury and prevent the splint from moving, but loose enough to permit circulation.

EXPERT TIP: If you suspect a victim has a broken bone, do not move the person unless the injured area is totally immobilised. If the skin is pierced, cover it with sterile dressings before immobilising the injury.

The Mysterious Effects of Lightning on the Body

South African researchers are conducting experiments to understand how the human body reacts to a lightning strike.

South Africa has about 500 deaths and thousands of injuries from lightning strikes each year, a much higher toll than other nations'. Johannesburg's subtropical climate means almost daily rain showers during the summer that, combined with its high elevation, makes the city particularly vulnerable to lightning.

In response, the University of the Witwatersrand in Johannesburg, better known as Wits University, has had a lightning research team since the 1960s. Recently, the electrical engineers and biomedical experts there have been pushing the boundaries of what is known about lightning deaths and injuries. The Wits scientists are trying to show exactly what happens to the human body when hit by lightning, which is not well understood.

'There is little literature on how different tissues are affected when struck by lightning,' observes Patrick Randolph-Quinney, a forensic anthropologist with Wits University. 'It has become a routine problem with the discovery of bodies in places where a lightning strike was likely. We haven't been able to say with certainty whether or not a lightning strike was indeed the cause of death.' But he adds that his team has found that lightning causes a specific pattern of cracking through the cellular structure of individual bone cells, indicating the passage of extreme levels of energy.

When it comes to lightning injuries, there has also been little research on the mechanisms of what happens to the human body when struck, other than well-established complications that can arise such as memory loss, insomnia and depression. To better understand these effects, and to work out why some parts of the body are damaged more than others, Wits electrical engineering graduate student Harry Lee is comparing the electrical conductivity of different human tissues.

Although the research is still in early stages, Lee says he expects to find dry skin to have a very low conductivity rate, which would explain why a person struck by lightning rarely has external burns. Alternatively, he expects to find fluid-based tissues, such as cerebrospinal fluid and mucous membranes to have higher conductivity rates.

'This work has potential to give scientists a way to look at the complex human body in a very different way,' Randolph-Quinney says. ■

Lightning Does Strike Twice
Contrary to the popular saying, lightning can and does strike the same place twice – especially if that place is tall, pointy and isolated. The Empire State Building in New York City is hit nearly 100 times a year.

Lightning flashes in the sky over Hong Kong. Thunderstorms are particularly common in subtropical places, where rain showers are an almost daily occurrence.

A woman crosses the black and white swirling pattern of a pavement in Lisbon, Portugal. This photo was taken from the historical elevator, Santa Justa.

Yo-yos

The popular spinning disc on a string probably originated in China, but the first known mention was in Greece around the fifth century B.C. The toys, made of wood, metal, or terra-cotta, were simply called discs. A vase from this era depicts a youth playing with one of these toys.

A likely origin for its name comes from Tagalog, the language of the Filipinos, who had a weapon called a yo-yo – a disk that was hurled at prey and then retrieved by a piece of string. Through the 19th century, it gained popularity as a toy in Europe and the United States. In the 1920s, a Filipino named Pedro Flores started a yo-yo company in California and started performing tricks. ■

Northern Wheatear

Oenanthe oenanthe

LENGTH: 14.5–16.0 cm (5.7–6.3 in)
WINGSPAN: 26–32 cm (10.0–12.5 in)

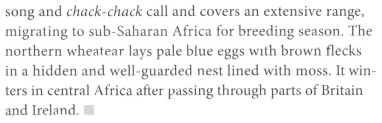

A small, ground-dwelling bird, the northern wheatear feeds mainly on insects and larvae. It sings a crackly song and *chack-chack* call and covers an extensive range, migrating to sub-Saharan Africa for breeding season. The northern wheatear lays pale blue eggs with brown flecks in a hidden and well-guarded nest lined with moss. It winters in central Africa after passing through parts of Britain and Ireland. ■

Surfing

Few people study wave energy more avidly than those who hope to catch a ride on it. What they're looking for is a big, powerful wave with a distinct shape that breaks cleanly and slides into shore.

Surfers keep an eye out for high-energy waves by studying forecasts for storms at sea – the strong, steady, far-reaching winds that might create a swell, a series of waves that can travel many miles over deep water. These carry a lot more energy than is produced by local winds lashing coastal waters. Web sites used by surfers predict wave energy as a function of wave height and the 'period', the time between wave crests. The greater the period, the faster the wave is moving.

Surfers also get to know the undersea topography of their local surf spots, which determines where and how the waves break. They understand that as a swell approaches shore, it will slow down and dramatically change shape in shallow areas. Some areas create especially big or interesting waves, like the Banzai Pipeline in Oahu, Hawaii. Eventually the wave falls over – 'breaks' – releasing energy into roaring sound and the movement of sand and water as it returns to sea in undertow and rip currents. Surfers use rip currents to ride back out, where the forces of gravity and buoyancy counteract to keep them afloat until their next wave. ■

The alien landscape of Canyonlands National Park, Utah, USA, viewed from Mesa Arch as the first rays of sunlight peep through an overcast sky.

COLOURS BURST IN WILD EXPLOSIONS; / FIERY, FLAMING SHADES OF FALL

OCTOBER

Kerala, India
Slow life down with a ride among elephants and temples.

A houseboat drifts slowly by on the Kerala backwaters, India. After the monsoon season ends, cycling is the perfect way to explore this beautiful region.

Time slows in Kerala. This narrow region of southern India, between the Arabian Sea and the Western Ghats, is one of the country's most diverse, crammed with history, wildlife and changing landscapes, from cool verdant tea plantations to golden tropical beaches. In the autumn, after the monsoon rains are over, tourists are fewer and prices drop. Autumn's cooler days allow visitors the perfect chance to take Kerala in like many locals do: by bike.

Peter Bluck, a Kerala cycling guide, notes that most roads are paved, making it possible to wind through villages, visit centuries-old forts or Hindu temples, spot elephants, watch the thatched *kettuvallam* houseboats drift downriver or just enjoy a perfect cup of tea. Bluck calls Kerala 'the friendliest state in India.' Kerala's famous spices and abundant coconuts give the region a reputation for one of India's most exciting cuisines, especially vegetarian food and spicy Chettinad curries – perfect for refueling after a long day's ride. ■

Diamonds in Space

Ten million tons of diamonds may be stored in Saturn and Jupiter. In those giant planets, the intense temperature and pressure may be able to convert atmospheric methane gas directly into diamonds, which rain down into their interiors. In the depths of Jupiter, conditions are so extreme that the gems may form an ocean of liquid diamond.

Caterpillar's Bad Breath Scares Off Predators

Manduca sexta
LIFESPAN. 30 50 days
ADULT WINGSPAN:
9.5–12.0 cm
(3.7–4.7 in)
RANGE: North America

The foul-breathed tobacco hornworm may not get many dates, but the odour keeps predators at bay. Scientists have found that this caterpillar can recycle the nicotene in tobacco plants to ward off hungry birds.

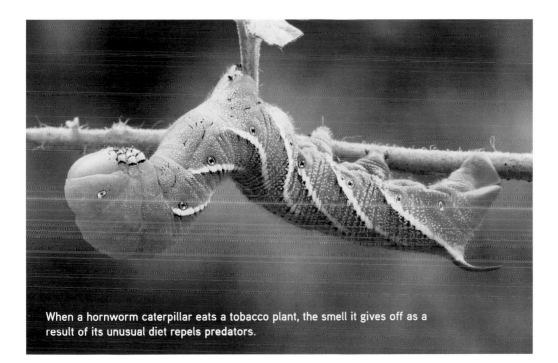

When a hornworm caterpillar eats a tobacco plant, the smell it gives off as a result of its unusual diet repels predators.

The key to the hornworm's halitosis is nicotine, a toxin it ingests while eating tobacco leaves. Experiments show that the caterpillar repurposes the nicotine, moving it from the gut to the haemolymph, the fluid in its circulatory system. The hornworm then excretes the excess nicotine when it exhales.

Wolf spiders and other predators of the hornworm don't have defences against nicotine and find the breath repulsive – and potentially poisonous, notes study leader Ian Baldwin, an ecologist at the Max Planck Institute for Chemical Ecology in Germany.

Nicotine, whose main role is for defence in tobacco plants, targets the neuromuscular junction – the place where nerve cells meet muscles – in animals. When an animal eats a plant containing nicotine its ability to breathe and move is impaired.

But the tobacco hornworm is a mysterious exception. As its name suggests, the caterpillar regularly dines on nicotine-containing plants, yet it doesn't seem to suffer any ill effects. Baldwin and his colleagues were investigating how the hornworms worked their chemical magic when they stumbled upon the importance of its bad breath. ■

STRANGE ... BUT TRUE   Nicotine is named after Jean Nicot, a French ambassador who brought tobacco to the French court as a medicine in the mid-16th century.

High stakes balancing act: A tightrope artist walks along a five-centimetre-thick (two inch) cable without a balancing pole in Zugspitze, Bavaria, Germany.

In Need of 'Sausage and Mash'? Visit an ATM.

Visitors to East London in search of a cash machine while attending the 2012 Summer Olympics might have been puzzled by an ATM on Commercial Street.

Tap the screen and a prompt pops up: English or Cockney? If Cockney is chosen, the next prompt advises the customer in search of 'fast sausage and mash' (cash) to select the amount. Among the options are a 'Lady Godiva' (£5), 'speckled hen' (£10), or 'horn of plenty' (£20), to be dispensed after the customer enters a 'Huckleberry Finn' (PIN).

The Cockney cash machine was the idea of Bank Machine, an ATM operator based in the United Kingdom. 'We wanted to introduce something fun and of local interest to our London machines,' a company official explained when the machines were launched a few years ago.

No one is certain when Cockney rhyming slang became the verbal currency of the East End, but British lexicographer Jonathon Green, author of *Cassell's Rhyming Slang*, guesses it was around the 1820s or '30s. Rhyming slang, he says, was created by market traders, or costermongers, in part for the sheer pleasure of playing with language but also, more subversively, as a way of talking over the heads of authorities and the police. In Cockney rhyming slang, a common word is replaced by a

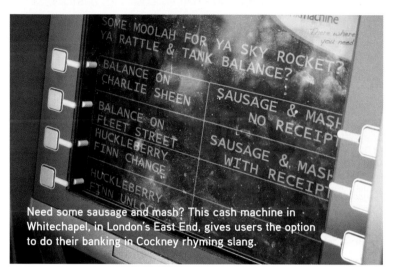

Need some sausage and mash? This cash machine in Whitechapel, in London's East End, gives users the option to do their banking in Cockney rhyming slang.

rhyming phrase – and traditionally, the secondary rhyming word is omitted. For example, to 'use your loaf' (short for 'loaf of bread') in rhyming slang means to use your head.

Like much else in the world, Cockney slang has been commercialised. 'It's like tourist London,' says Green. 'Think black cabs and red buses.' It's also, predictably, been Hollywoodised (think Audrey Hepburn as Eliza Doolittle, Bert the Chimney Sweep in *Mary Poppins* or any of Guy Ritchie's bumbling thugs). There's even an app – TripLingo UK Edition, a cyber-translator with a Cockney option. And for those in search of 'bread and honey' (money) – they can get cash from one of 16 Cockney-speaking ATMs in East London. ▪

All That Glitters
Instead of snacks, a peculiar vending machine in Abu Dhabi, United Arab Emirates, dispenses 24-carat-gold bars and coins.

Wuffy the Dog
Keeping an eye out for her feline friends

As a general rule, dogs and cats tend to not get along. But one rescued golden retriever named Wuffy never really bought into that rivalry—in fact, she helped take care of sick and abandoned cats and kittens!

When Wuffy brought four abandoned kittens to her owner, Gary Rohde, he thought it was just a coincidence (a very cute one). But Wuffy seemed to have all the instincts of a mother cat; she kept a watchful eye over her adopted family, knew when they were hungry or thirsty, taught them how to go to the bathroom and gave them tongue baths. Her little litter grew up strong, healthy and playful.

Wuffy's affinity for cats didn't stop with those first four kittens. For more than ten years, she helped care for her feline friends by working with Southern California Siamese Rescue. She helped rehabilitate hundreds of sick and injured cats during her time there.

But Wuffy wasn't just a cat lady—she got along well with dogs too, and was still keeping up with the puppies when she was 16 years old. Cats, dogs and humans are all united in her fan club. ▪

Wuffy the cat-loving dog with one of her feline friends. Wuffy helped hundreds of cats and kittens in her time at Southern California Siamese Rescue, in the USA.

How To: Make a Rope
Rope is useful for everything from building a shelter to rappelling down a cliff.

  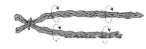  

1 Test possible materials (grass, vine, stringy bark etc.) by knotting a piece. If it doesn't break, it's usable.

2 Lay strands – one slightly shorter than the other – parallel to each other and knot them together at one end. Divide in half.

3 Twist each half once clockwise.

4 Twist halves together anti-clockwise. Repeat steps 3 and 4, splicing in a new string as the shorter half runs out (make sure to overlap by at least 8 centimetres [3 in]).

5 Make a stronger rope by braiding three of these ropes together.

EXPERT TIP: If you find a natural shelter, look for tracks, scat or other signs that an animal has used it recently. Avoid these shelters, as the animal may be coming back and it may be dangerous.

Can Dogs Feel Our Emotions?

We may share many things with our dogs, but our emotions might be contagious. A recent study suggests that man's best friend may mirror their owners' feelings.

We all know yawns are contagious, but it's not just between humans. New dog owners who claim their pets know their feelings may be onto something: a study has shown that canines yawn more in response to their owners' yawns than to strangers' yawns. That suggests dogs are 'emotionally connected' to people, asserts the study's leader, Teresa Romero of the University of Tokyo.

Scientists already knew that dogs sometimes yawn when they see people yawn, but it was unclear if that was considered a form of empathy or mild stress, as yawning can be caused by anxiety. So, Romero and her team set up an experiment in which 25 pet dogs of various breeds watched both their owners and strangers yawn or pretend to yawn.

The team ruled out stress when researchers saw no significant differences in the dogs' heartbeats during the experiments. According to the study, not only did the dogs in the study yawn more in response to their owners' yawns, they also yawned less when they saw fake yawns, suggesting they were exhibiting true contagious yawning.

Contagious yawning occurs in humans, chimpanzees, baboons and dogs. In a similar study published in 2013, scientists found that people yawn more in response to the yawns of people they care about most. The scientists suspect that contagious yawning is a form of empathising with people experiencing a feeling, which – in the case of yawning – usually means stress, anxiety, boredom, or fatigue. By reenacting the behaviour, a person is essentially sharing emotions with the original yawner. The 'contagious yawn' response is more likely to occur with those people one already empathises with often. It's the same social bond that makes you sad when a friend or loved one is upset.

Elisabetta Palagi of the Institute of Cognitive Sciences and Technologies in Rome notes that Romero's study is the first time that scientists have shown contagious yawning occurring between different species. 'This could be the result of a long process of domestication,' suggests Palagi, who wasn't involved in the study. 'Once more,' she says, the study 'demonstrates that dogs are capable of empathic abilities toward humans.' ■

Keep a Cool Head
Yawning might help you cool off – literally. Working in tandem, the jaw and sinuses act like a bellows, pumping fresh air onto the brain to lower its temperature so it can work efficiently. This discovery could help doctors treat insomnia, migraines and other medical conditions.

Scientists say dogs yawn in response to their owners' yawns more so than a stranger's. Does this prove an emotional connection between dogs and people?

A dramatic composite image of the Ring Nebula, created by combining visible-light observations by the Hubble Space Telescope with infrared data from the ground-based Large Binocular Telescope.

Suits

The word 'suit' derives from the French verb *suivre,* 'to follow' and applies to items that are meant to be used together, including matching clothing. Although they look nothing alike, today's suits are the progeny of medieval armour.

In 1666, King Charles II established court dress consisting of a coat, waistcoat and knee breeches in the same material. But the new garb didn't suit the upper-class English lifestyle, which centred on riding and hunting. English gentry therefore shortened the jacket front and used plain, sturdy cloth instead of embroidered silks, all to make horse riding easier.

Suiting changed even more in the 1800s. George Bryan 'Beau' Brummel befriended the future King George IV and encouraged his tailors to use quieter colours in weaves that would stand the test of time, to become the suits we know today. ■

Night Vision Goggles

Humans and other mammals have rods in the retina of the eye – millions of tiny cylindrical elements that contain rhodopsin, a purple pigment that can detect dim light. We also have retinal cones – light-sensitive cells that enable us to read fine print. Nocturnal creatures, however, such as cats, lemurs and owls, have only rods, which makes them capable of seeing far better than humans in low light.

Since we don't have the eyesight of creatures of the night, technology must come to our aid. Night vision binoculars and scopes are electro-optical instruments that are incredibly sensitive to a broad range of light, from visible through infrared. Light that enters a lens in a night vision scope reflects off an image intensifier to a photocathode and is converted to an electronic image.

Amplified on a viewing screen, the image reveals much more than a night scene observed through a conventional scope. Like cameras, these devices have various magnifications. They're especially valuable, for example, during night operations involving close air support of ground troops. ■

Common Quail

Coturnix coturnix
LENGTH: 16–18 cm (6.3–7.1 in)
WINGSPAN: 32–35 cm (12.6–13.8 in)

The common quail prefers dry, sunny, open fields, where it eats seeds and insects off the ground. A small, round bird, its drab colouring and reluctance to fly make it notoriously difficult to spot in grass. When startled into flight, the common quail makes a *wree* sound as it spreads its long wings before quickly returning to the ground. Its call can be heard most in the mornings and evenings. ■

A 13-year-old Kazakh girl learns how to hunt with her golden eagle in western Mongolia. Ashol-Pan, daughter of a celebrated hunter, may be the first girl to learn this traditional skill.

NO

THE AUTUMN AIR IS CLEAR, / THE AUTUMN MOON IS BRIGHT

VEMBER

Phnom Penh, Cambodia

Revel at the city's autumn festival as it engulfs streets and waterways.

Longboats take part in the annual Bon Om Tuk festival, in Phnom Penh, Cambodia. The Water and Moon Festival also honours the start of fishing season.

A visitor to this exotic Asian capital channels the merging pulses of the city's troubled past and vibrant present. Yearly, its heady scents and sights kick into overdrive for Bon Om Touk, the three-day Water and Moon Festival. It's a chaotic but friendly celebration, with fairground rides, fireworks, drinking, pop music and traditional Khmer dancing. In darker times, the Khmer Rouge banned Bon Om Touk, but today the exuberance that infuses the festivities is contagious.

Be sure to bring your appetite – and adventurous spirit – as you sample such local delicacies from food stands as refreshing sticky rice with mango and fried tarantulas. Then, along with two and a half million other revellers, make your way to the Royal Palace to cheer on local boat-racing teams.

Bon Om Touk also honours the changing direction of the Tonlé Sap River and the start of fishing season. You'll understand why after you've tasted some fish amok, Cambodia's rich, coconutty national dish. ■

Chameleons' Colourful Body Language

Chameleons are famed for their ability to change colour and many think that this helps them to camouflage to hide from predators. But it might have more to do with communication. Scientists found that the brightness of male chameleons' stripes predicted how likely they were to start a fight with a rival male and the brightness of their heads predicted their odds of winning.

My Oh My, What Deep Origins You Have

Do you think you know the story of Little Red Riding Hood?

The story of Little Red Riding Hood occurs in various forms in folk tales from many different cultures, but what are its origins?

It's a story told around the world. Little Red Riding Hood goes to visit her grandmother, only to discover that a wolf has eaten the old lady, dressed in her clothes and now plans to eat the little girl, too. The end of the story depends on which version you hear – was Little Red Riding Hood eaten? Or did a passing huntsman save her?

Elements of the story vary from place to place as well. In parts of Iran, the child in peril is a boy, because little girls wouldn't wander out on their own. In Africa, the villain could be a fox or a hyena.

But where does this story come from? Scholars have been puzzling over the roots of Little Red Riding Hood for years. Jamie Tehrani, an anthropologist at Durham University, thinks he's found the answer by applying methods used to track the evolution of biological species to the evolution of folk tales.

Many assume that Charles Perrault, who wrote the story down in the 17th century, was its creator. But, although most versions that we're familiar with today descended from Perrault's tale, he didn't invent it. Others argue that the folk tale came from Asia, but Tehrani's analysis shows that Asian variations are more like the modern fairy tale, as they contain the famous 'What big eyes you have!' line.

That dialogue is missing from what Tehrani believes is the original source. 'There's an 11th-century poem from Belgium that was recorded by a priest, who says there's this tale told by the local peasants about a girl wearing a red baptism tunic who wanders off and encounters this wolf,' Tehrani notes. He also believes there's a bigger question at hand, about human imagination. 'These folk tales are a good way of reading what we really care about.' ∎

STRANGE ... BUT TRUE A wolf pup's eyes appear blue at birth, but they turn yellow by the time it is eight months old.

Forked lightning, exploding lava bombs and ash clouds create this dramatic scene as the Sakurajima volcano erupts in Kyushu, Japan.

From Kate Winslet to Jelly Doughnuts, Weird Names Abound

When you have to name hundreds of new species at once, it pays to get creative.

While taxonomists – scientists who describe and name species – try to bestow descriptive names on new organisms, there is also ample evidence that they like to have fun with the task.

Quentin Wheeler and colleague Kelly Miller are responsible for the *Gelae* genus of slime-mould beetles, which feed on the immature, jellylike stage of slime moulds. The Gelae genus includes the species *Gelae donut, Gelae baen, Gelae fish* and *Gelae rol*. Terry Erwin, an insect researcher who specialises in beetles at the Smithsonian National Museum of Natural History, has named almost 300 species in a genus of beetles called *Agra*. Among them are two species named *Agra vation* and *Agra vate*. Erwin insists he wasn't particularly annoyed when he named the two sister species. 'It was just to use aggravation because it went with *Agra*,' he says. The genus also includes *Agra katewinsletae*, named for the actress in the movie *Titanic* and *Agra liv*, named for Liv Tyler for her part in the movie *Armageddon*. Since all new species descriptions must be published in a peer-reviewed scientific journal, getting unusual names past colleagues is crucial. Nevertheless, there is a striped octopus species found around the Indonesian archipelago named *Wunderpus photogenicus* and a genus of tiny marine snail called *Ittibittium*. ■

Tongue-Twister The longest name in the English language – at 189,819 letters – is the chemical name for the protein titin. It takes about three hours to pronounce the full word.

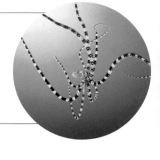

Merlin the Dolphin

The tech-obsessed marine mammal

Forget leaping in the air or chasing after his friends. When Merlin the dolphin wants to play, it's all about technology: he plays games on an iPad!

Dolphin researcher Jack Kassewitz created a game app for the iPad called 'Same, Different,' just for Merlin. First, Kassewitz shows the dolphin an image on the iPad, such as a yellow rubber duck toy. After Merlin touches the image with his beak, he swims away to find a real toy duck. Merlin gets so excited he gives the researcher a 'pec tap', a sort of high five with his pectoral fin.

The tasks are easy for Merlin, as dolphins are regularly recognised as one of the most intelligent animals. Kassewitz says that learning the software is an important building block toward comprehensive interspecies communication.

Kassewitz hopes that iPad games such as this one will one day lead to a shared language between humans and dolphins based on symbols, similar to how some apes communicate with people. 'Dolphin communication skills are very advanced,' he says. 'With Merlin's help, we can teach people that we're only co-owners of this planet with other intelligent species.' ■

Merlin is one computer savvy dolphin, who loves using his iPad to play a game created especially for him, and to communicate with his trainer.

How To: Carry a Fire

If you need to move your campsite, hang onto your fire with these tips.

1 To move embers from one spot to the next while travelling, or keep embers ready for starting signal fires, find a metal soft-drink or similar can or another nonburnable receptacle (Native Americans used animal horns). With a sharp object, poke holes in the sides.

2 Place a layer of slow-burning material such as moss in the bottom of the can. Place the embers on top of the moss.

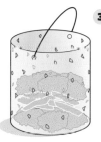

3 Place another layer of slow-burning material on top of the embers. Don't pack them too loosely or too tightly. The former will cause the embers to flare; the latter will suffocate the fire.

EXPERT TIP: Hardwoods such as oak, hickory, birch and ash produce a long-burning fire with lasting coals. Softwoods like pine, spruce, cedar and aspen produce a quick, hot fire and make good fuel for starting a longer-burning fire with harder wood.

A Lake on Mars Could Have Supported Life Billions of Years Ago

The Mars rover Curiosity team describes an ancient, watery landscape.

The fossil remains of a lake on Mars that could have supported life have been identified not far from where NASA's Curiosity rover landed in 2012. Inside Gale Crater on Mars, the rover science team has found chemical and mineral conditions needed for life, mission scientists report. As if that finding weren't dramatic enough, the scientists said that the ancient lake, which existed for as long as tens of thousands of years, was just one part of a watery Martian environment that also included streams and subsurface groundwater. In such a place, life could have survived for tens of millions of years.

The Curiosity rover team's findings add substantially to the understanding of Gale Crater – a meteorite impact site that the Mars rover has been exploring – as a once habitable environment, the first ever found on Mars. 'With this finding, we're a significant step closer to understanding how to locate environments on Mars that can support life,' says project scientist John Grotzinger of NASA's Jet Propulsion Laboratory in Pasadena, California.

Yellowknife Bay, a small section of Gale Crater first described as suitable for ancient microbial life even before the surrounding lake was discovered, is located near Curiosity's landing site. Exploring the area was never considered a primary goal for the rover, but an early detour to Yellowknife Bay proved to be a scientific bonanza, turning into a months-long stay. The key to the discovery was the detection of substantial amounts of clay – a soil type that can be formed only in the presence of water – in the stone. The clay appears to have formed at Yellowknife when it was covered by water, rather than being blown in or brought by a stream.

The kind of microbes that could have survived the conditions of Gale Crater are known as chemolithotrophs – organisms that get their 'food' from the electron transfer of chemical compounds in rocks. They can live without sunlight on Earth and would potentially be similarly capable on Mars.

Grotzinger and others emphasise that, while the finding that Gale Crater was habitable is a major step forward in the search for extraterrestrial life, it does not necessarily mean that organisms ever actually lived there. ■

Ready for My Close-Up
Curiosity has 17 cameras that can take pictures as tiny as 12.5 microns. That's smaller than the width of a human hair.

Scientists believe that water flowed for centuries into the Gale Crater on Mars. The ancient waterway may have looked like this.

A climber crosses a ladder bridge through the Khumbu Icefall, Mount Everest, Nepal. Shifting ice exposes dangerous new crevasses with little warning.

Cologne

Eau de cologne ('water of Cologne') originated, as one might expect, in the German town for which it was named. In A.D. 50, the Romans established a colony called Colonia Agrippina, named for the emperor's wife. After the Franks took over, the name was shortened to Cologne and the town grew into a city best known for a product made by Italian barber Jean-Baptiste Farina, who settled there in 1709.

Farina created a light, alcohol-based perfume by blending orange bitters, lemon spirits and bergamot oil. He named it eau de Cologne and sold it to great acclaim. French soldiers stationed in Cologne during the Seven Years' War (1756–1763) took a liking to the scent and soon its reputation spread far and wide. ■

Bohemian Waxwing

Bombycilla garrulus
LENGTH: 18–21 cm (7–8 in)
WINGSPAN: 32–35 cm (12.6–13.8 in)

Larger and more grey than the cedar waxwing, the Bohemian waxwing nests in woodlands and feeds on insects, berries and other small fruits. It flutters from perch to perch on trees and bushes, rarely settling on the ground. Bohemian waxwings can be found in large flocks and are identified by their distinct buzzy trilling *zeee* call and bright red wing tips. ■

Suspension Bridges

Suspension bridges date back to the 15th century and comprise a deck, towers (called abutments) at either end and a network of cables that form a parabolic curve (a parabola is a curve formed by points that are at an equal distance from a fixed point and a fixed straight line). A main cable runs from tower to tower and vertical cables run off the main cable, supporting the weight of the deck and transferring it to the towers. The main cable is actually anchored beyond the abutments, to prevent the bridge structure from giving in to the force of compression. The weight of the bridge itself pulls inward on the towers and the cables counteract this with an equal force. In other words, compression from the bridge's deck and tension from the cables are balanced.

Because of their design, suspension bridges have many advantages. For one thing, they can span great distances. The longest suspension bridge in the world is the Akashi-Kaikyo Bridge in Japan, spanning an impressive 3,911 metres (12,831 ft). ■

Cape Washington, Ross Sea, Antarctica: An Emperor Penguin becomes briefly airborne as it launches itself from the sea onto the edge of an ice flow.

DE

FROSTY DAYS AND ICE-STILL NIGHTS, / FIR TREES TRIMMED WITH TINY LIGHTS

CEMBER

The Gold Coast, Australia

Hang 10 on curling combers at Australia's surfing mecca.

Surfer's Paradise really is just that, with easterly swells rolling in from the Pacific producing 1–1.5-metre (3–5 ft) waves consistently from December to April.

With more than 64 kilometres (40 mi) of beaches, Queensland's Gold Coast, just south of Brisbane, offers some of the best, most reliable waves in Australia. From December to April, easterly swells rolling in from the Pacific produce 1–1.5-metre (3–5 ft) waves around the aptly named Surfer's Paradise, drawing hordes of surfers eager to test their skills.

Practice at one of the surf schools scattered along the coast. Board in hand, pad along golden sands. Strike into the sun-warmed waters at famed sites like the Spit, Rainbow Bay, or Burleigh Heads, whose right-hand point break produces long, tubular waves.

Paddle furiously to catch an incoming breaker. Shift onto your knees, then, shakily at first, stand up. For a brief moment, you're suspended between dazzling Aussie sunshine above and shimmering aquamarine waters below. The next second, you've wiped out as the wave crashes about you. But the instant you resurface and grab your board, you're charging offshore again, ready to catch the next perfect crest. ■

World's Oldest Calendar Discovered

Archaeologists in Scotland have uncovered what they believe to be a lunar calendar – a series of 12 large, specially shaped pits that were designed to mimic the various phases of the moon. The pits, which align with where the sun would have risen on the midwinter solstice, are nearly 10,000 years old, by far the oldest 'calendar' discovered so far.

Elephants Know How Dangerous We Are From How We Speak

Loxodonta africana
DIET: Herbivorous
LIFESPAN: Up to 70 years
WEIGHT: 2,250–6,350 kg (5,000–14,000 lb)

Elephants pay attention when we speak, a new study in Kenya shows.

A female forest elephant charges the scent of the photographer, while her mother protects a youngster in Dzanga Bai, Dzanga-Ndoki National Park, Central African Republic.

When an elephant killed a Maasai woman who was collecting firewood near Kenya's Amboseli National Park in 2007, a group of young Maasai men retaliated by spearing an elephant at random. Later, the animal died from his wounds.

Elephants experience those kinds of killings sporadically. Yet the attacks happen often enough that the tuskers have learned that the Maasai – and Maasai men in particular – are dangerous. The elephants in the Amboseli region are so aware of this that they can even distinguish between Ma, the language of the Maasai and other languages, says a team of researchers, who reported their findings in the *Proceedings of the National Academy of Sciences*.

The results add to 'our growing knowledge of the discriminatory abilities of the elephant mind, and how elephants make decisions and see their world,' says Joyce Poole, an elephant expert with ElephantVoices in Masai Mara, Kenya. Indeed, previous studies have shown that the Amboseli elephants can tell the cattle-herding, red-robed Maasai apart from their agricultural and more blandly dressed neighbours, the Kamba people, simply by scent and the colour of their dress. The elephants know, too, that walking through villages at weekends is dangerous, as is crop raiding during the full moon. ◼

STRANGE … BUT TRUE An elephant's brain weighs about 5 kilograms (11 lb) and it's larger than the brain of any other land animal.

Brandenburg, Germany, is balmy if you're in Tropical Islands, a theme park housed in a former aircraft hangar where the temperature is a perpetual 24 degrees Celsius (75°F).

Could Humans Hibernate?

Ever wished you could nap through the winter? Ask a fat-tailed dwarf lemur how it's done. These mini-primates could hold the key to modern hibernation.

These tiny animals have a talent that could help save human lives. Fat-tailed dwarf lemurs are the only primates that can hibernate – for now. But because they're genetically similar to humans, these animals may one day teach us how to hibernate.

Hibernation conjures up images of bears slumbering in caves, but it doesn't necessarily mean sleep. Hibernation simply refers to the seasonal bodily changes that occur in some animals – slower heart rates, decreased oxygen intake and more. If humans could do it, the practical applications would be limitless.

Consider terminally ill patients who will die without an organ transplant. With every breath, every heartbeat, they slip away. But during hibernation, a lemur breathes only once every 20 minutes and its heart rate drops to just four beats per minute. Do the same thing for the dying human and the patient could remain in this suspended state until a donor is found.

In humans, there are two different types of sleep: rapid eye movement (REM) sleep, which is when we dream, and non-REM sleep. Scientists believe that non-REM sleep has a replenishing effect on our bodies and we can't go long without it. There's a reason we spend one-third of our lives asleep.

But when lemurs hibernate, scientists speculate that they experience only REM sleep. 'If you completely deprive animals of [non-REM] sleep, then they die,' says Andrew Krystal, co-author of the study. 'And yet the lemurs that hibernate appear to be able to go for months without sleep . . . and they're not dying.'

The research could lead Krystal and his team closer to the answers they'll need to someday replicate the results in humans. 'There's a lot of mystery left,' Krystal admits. 'It raises this great question: can [lemurs] really go that long and survive without non-REM sleep?'. . . it's surprising. ■

A Bear of a Diet Bears can lose 25 to 40 percent of their body weight during hibernation – by burning large stores of fat for fuel. Some go as long as eight months without eating!

Mavis and Beau, Concierge Dogs

Working Like Dogs at a Vancouver Hotel

Guests at the Fairmont Hotel in Vancouver, British Columbia, don't get greeted only by a doorman. They're also met by Mavis, a golden retriever, and Beau, a yellow Labrador. When their first jobs as Seeing Eye dogs didn't work out, Mavis and Beau began working at the Fairmont.

Hotel staff say that these canine ambassadors are by far the most popular employees of the hotel. Paid in hot dogs, apples and belly rubs, the pair get 'hired' to do jobs like going for walks and playing in the park with hotel guests.

Mavis and Beau are on duty next to the concierge desk to meet and greet guests from kids to Hollywood elite alike. Halle Berry, Robin Williams and Cindy Crawford are among the hundreds of people who have had their pictures taken with Mavis and Beau. Every guest, regardless of how famous, gets welcomed in with a friendly bark. The hotel welcomes dogs as guests as well and

Mavis and Beau, pictured hard at work at the Fairmount Hotel in Vancouver, Canada, meet and greet guests, shake a paw or take a walk with the guests.

Mavis and Beau even helped pick out the room service menu items for their canine guests.

When she's not working, Mavis chews her stuffed dog (which looks exactly like her) and checks her email . . . sort of. 'Guests like to send her photos of their playtime with Mavis,' says Lynn Gervais, who works at the hotel. 'So she has her own personal email address.' ■

How To: Make a Temple Fire

A temple fire can be useful when the ground is unsuitable for fire building.

1 Drive four green sticks – each 8–10 centimetres (3–4 in) in diameter and up to a metre (2–3 ft) long and with forked ends – into wet or snow-covered ground.

2 Lash green crosspieces between the tops of the four sticks, using the forks to help hold the crosspieces in place.

3 Place a layer of closely packed green logs (so as not to burn) atop the crosspieces.

4 Cover the green logs with 10–20 centimetres (several inches) of earth. Light a fire atop the elevated earthen base and suspend your cooking pot over the fire with a pole supported by two Y-shaped branches.

EXPERT TIP: To light a fire efficiently, leave an air space under the top bar of a triangle of kindling. Lay a handful of tinder upright against the top stick. Hold a match beneath the tinder until the flame burns up through it, then place additional tinder and kindling onto the fire.

Nature Boosts Creativity and Health

Take some time to stop and smell the roses.

Richard Louv coined the term 'nature-deficit disorder' to describe the loss of connection children increasingly feel with the natural world. Nature-deficit disorder is not a clinically recognised condition, he explains, but rather a term to evoke a loss of communion with other living things. Nevertheless, he argues, nature-deficit disorder affects 'health, spiritual well-being and many other areas, including [people's] ability to feel ultimately alive.'

The causes of the disorder include loss of open space, increasingly busy schedules, an emphasis on team sports over individual play and exploration, and what Louv and others call a 'culture of fear', in which people are afraid to visit natural areas or even go outside due to heavy media coverage of violent events.

As of 2008, more people now live in cities than in the countryside. Louv believes that marked a huge moment in human history and it means one of two things: either the human connection to nature continuing to fade or the beginning of a new kind of city. One way to achieve the latter is through 'biophilic', or nature-inspired design, which Louv describes as the incorporation of nature where we live, work, learn and play, not only as something we drive an hour to visit.

Louv has written about the impacts of 'nature time' on problems like anxiety, depression, attention deficit disorder (ADD) and obesity, and he argues that nature is a good antidote to all of them. 'I didn't coin it, but I like the phrase "Sitting is the new smoking,"' Louv says, 'because new evidence shows that sitting long hours every day can have serious health risks similar to those caused by smoking.'

Researchers at the University of Illinois are investigating whether time in the woods could be used to supplement treatment of ADD. A study at the University of Kansas found that young people who backpacked for three days showed higher creativity and cognitive abilities. Hospital patients who can see a natural landscape have been shown to recover more quickly, as well. 'As an antidote,' says Louv, 'we need to figure out ways to increase nature time even as technology increases. It has to be a conscious decision.' ■

Bringing Nature to You
Houseplants are more than just a source of greenery – they have health benefits. Plants remove up to 87 percent of volatile organic compounds from the air every 24 hours and release water and oxygen into the room.

The term 'nature-deficit disorder' is used to describe a condition of separation from nature, when people are reluctant to venture out into the countryside.

Phan Thiet, Binh Thuan,
Vietnam: After hours playing
with their kites on the dune,
these boys run and slide down
from the top to head home.

Santa Claus

Around A.D. 280, a child named Nicholas was born to a wealthy family in Turkey. Known for his generosity, legends say he gave away his inheritance, became a monk and travelled far and wide helping others. His feast day is celebrated on 6 December.

In Holland, children celebrate St. Nicholas Day by putting their shoes out to receive sweets from St. Nick. The Dutch call him Sinter Klaas and as settlers brought their traditions to the New World, the name became Santa Claus.

In 1822, Clement Clarke Moore wrote a poem called *An Account of a Visit from St. Nicholas*, describing Santa Claus as a portly figure with magical abilities. In 1881, a cartoonist illustrated Moore's poem with a cartoon of Santa as a jolly, bearded man in a bright red suit carrying a sack of toys. ■

Pintail

Anas acuta

LENGTH: 51–62 cm (20–24 in)

WINGSPAN: 80–95 cm (31.5–37.5 in)

A graceful, long-necked duck, the northern pintail is sometimes called the 'greyhound of the air'. It nests in open, shallow wetlands in both fresh and estuarine habitats, feeding on grain, seeds, snails and aquatic insects from the ground and water. Males whistle a *kwee-hee* call, while the female's call is a muffled *quack*. The pintail winters near the equator in sub-Saharan Africa, Asia and South America. ■

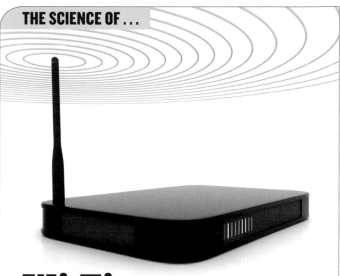

Wi-Fi

The term Wi-Fi is actually a brand name of sorts for a standard more formally known as 802.11 networking, or just 'wireless networking'. The Institute of Electrical and Electronics Engineers (IEEE) is in charge of setting standards for this and other protocols.

So what is Wi-Fi? It's a means of wireless communication that works like a radio. An adapter inside a computer converts data into a radio signal and transmits it via an antenna. On the other end of the transmission, a router receives the signal and converts it back into data. This pathway can be between a device (such as a laptop computer) and the Internet or vice versa.

However, Wi-Fi is not just a fancy radio. It operates at a higher frequency than traditional radio waves, which gives it more data capacity. And Wi-Fi has the ability to hop from frequency to frequency, which means that multiple devices can use just one router. For the most part, Wi-Fi networks are easy to set up and maintain, are reliable and are even easier to connect to; that's why nearly every hotel, airport, library and coffee shop these days boasts free Wi-Fi access. ■

2015 Calendar

January
S	M	T	W	T	F	S
				1	2	3
4	5	6	7	8	9	10
11	12	13	14	15	16	17
18	19	20	21	22	23	24
25	26	27	28	29	30	31

February
S	M	T	W	T	F	S
1	2	3	4	5	6	7
8	9	10	11	12	13	14
15	16	17	18	19	20	21
22	23	24	25	26	27	28

March
S	M	T	W	T	F	S
1	2	3	4	5	6	7
8	9	10	11	12	13	14
15	16	17	18	19	20	21
22	23	24	25	26	27	28
29	30	31				

April
S	M	T	W	T	F	S
			1	2	3	4
5	6	7	8	9	10	11
12	13	14	15	16	17	18
19	20	21	22	23	24	25
26	27	28	29	30		

May
S	M	T	W	T	F	S
					1	2
3	4	5	6	7	8	9
10	11	12	13	14	15	16
17	18	19	20	21	22	23
24/31	25	26	27	28	29	30

June
S	M	T	W	T	F	S
	1	2	3	4	5	6
7	8	9	10	11	12	13
14	15	16	17	18	19	20
21	22	23	24	25	26	27
28	29	30				

July
S	M	T	W	T	F	S
			1	2	3	4
5	6	7	8	9	10	11
12	13	14	15	16	17	18
19	20	21	22	23	24	25
26	27	28	29	30	31	

August
S	M	T	W	T	F	S
						1
2	3	4	5	6	7	8
9	10	11	12	13	14	15
16	17	18	19	20	21	22
23/30	24/31	25	26	27	28	29

September
S	M	T	W	T	F	S
		1	2	3	4	5
6	7	8	9	10	11	12
13	14	15	16	17	18	19
20	21	22	23	24	25	26
27	28	29	30			

October
S	M	T	W	T	F	S
				1	2	3
4	5	6	7	8	9	10
11	12	13	14	15	16	17
18	19	20	21	22	23	24
25	26	27	28	29	30	31

November
S	M	T	W	T	F	S
1	2	3	4	5	6	7
8	9	10	11	12	13	14
15	16	17	18	19	20	21
22	23	24	25	26	27	28
29	30					

December
S	M	T	W	T	F	S
		1	2	3	4	5
6	7	8	9	10	11	12
13	14	15	16	17	18	19
20	21	22	23	24	25	26
27	28	29	30	31		

Resources

National Geographic Books

National Geographic Books is a global publisher of 125 new books annually in Adult and Children's combined, as well as a publisher of digital content and services with more than 50 partners who translate our books. For more information on National Geographic Books, visit facebook.com/NatGeoBooks and nationalgeographic.com/books.

National Geographic magazine

National Geographic magazine has a long tradition of combining on-the-ground reporting with award-winning photography to inform people about life on our planet. It has won 12 National Magazine Awards in the past seven years: for Best Tablet Edition in 2012; Magazine of the Year and Single-Topic Issue in 2011; for General Excellence, Photojournalism and Essays, plus two Digital Media Awards for Best Photography and Best Community, in 2010; for Photojournalism in 2009; and for General Excellence, Photojournalism and Reporting in 2008.

The magazine is the official journal of the National Geographic Society, one of the world's largest nonprofit education and scientific organisations. Published in English and 37 local-language editions, the magazine has a global circulation of around 8 million. It is sent each month to National Geographic members and is available on newsstands for £5.50 a copy. Single copies can be ordered by calling 3120-487-4115, also the number to call for membership to the Society.

To submit a favourite photo for possible publication in *National Geographic* magazine, visit the Your Shot page at http://ngm.national geographic.com/your-shot/your-shot.

National Geographic Traveler magazine

National Geographic Traveler: All travel, all the time. *National Geographic Traveler* is the world's most widely read travel magazine. Published eight times a year, Traveler is available by subscription (3120-487-4115). Its website is at www.nationalgeographic .com/traveler.

National Geographic Digital Media

National Geographic Digital Media (NGDM) is the multimedia division of National Geographic Ventures. Holding many top industry awards, NGDM publishes Nationalgeographic .com, including its daily online news service. With a focus on developments in the fields of science, nature and cultures, National Geographic's *Daily News* provides access to the top stories that are changing our world. For more information, visit http://news.national geographic.com/news/.

Text Credits

Reprinted by arrangement from the book *125 True Stories of Amazing Animals.* Copyright © 2012 National Geographic Society. 8, 'Bison Buddy'; 14, 'Pig Athletes'; 23, 'Fish Scores Goal'; 31, 'Rabbit Joins Hospital Staff'; 35, 'Penguin Becomes Knight'; 51, 'Chimp Outsmarts Humans'; 71, 'Workin' Like a Dog'; 87, 'Smart Dog'; 92, 'Dolphin Plays With iPad'

Reprinted by arrangement from the book *An Uncommon History of Common Things* by Bethanne Patrick and John Thompson. Copyright © 2009 National Geographic Society. 15, 'Sandwich'; 65, 'Santa Claus'; 119, 'Applause'; 121, 'Birthday Cake'; 121, 'Toasting'; 147, 'Air Conditioning'; 156, 'Swimming Pool'; 161, 'Suit'; 192, 'Soap'; 220, 'Marbles'; 209, 'Cologne'; 222, 'Yo-Yo'

Reprinted by arrangement from the book *Complete Survival Manual* by Michael S. Sweeny. Copyright © 2009 National Geographic Society. 19, 'How To: Make Rope from Natural Materials'; 32, 'How To: Make a Line and Hook'; 37, 'How To: Splint a Broken Bone'; 46, 'How To: Make a Temple Fire'; 92, 'How To: Make a Deadfall Trap'; 129, 'How To: Survive Quicksand'; 139, 'How To: Carry a Fire'; 143, 'How To: Build a Snowtrench'; 177 'How To: Get Water From a Cactus'; 190, 'How To: Sun-Dry Meat'; 268, 'How To: Fight Off a Shark'; 270, 'How To: Make a Floating Device From Pants While Treading Water'

Reprinted by arrangement from the book *Science of Everything.* Copyright © 2013 National Geographic Society. 35, 'Conservation of Energy: Roller Coaster'; 59, 'Surfing'; 69, 'Bernouli's Principle: Hovercraft'; 74, 'Fireworks'; 82, 'Magnetic Fields: Home Plumbing System'; 106, 'Thunderstorms'; 129, 'Suspension Bridge'; 220, 'Night Vision Goggles'; 246, 'Wi-Fi'; 293, 'Macromolecular Chemistry: Superglue'; 362, "Immunobiology: Allergies; 375, 'Robotic Surgery'

Illustrations Credits

Cover, Seth Casteel's Underwater Dogs/Little, Brown and Company/TandemStock.com; Back Cover, Jimmy Chin and Lynsey Dyer/National Geographic Creative; 2-3, Val Shevchenko/Shutterstock; 4-5, Wes C. Skiles; 6, Liam Carroll/National Geographic Your Shot; 8, Vincent J. Musi/National Geographic Creative; 10-11, Derek Spear/National Geographic Your Shot; 12 (LE), O. Louis Mazzatenta/National Geographic Creative; 12 (RT), Susan Schmitz/Shutterstock; 13 (LE), Ralph Lee Hopkins/National Geographic Creative; 13 (UPRT), Heidi Kristensen/iStockphoto; 13 (LORT), GlobalP/iStockphoto; 14-15, Kacper Kowalski/Aeromedia.pl/Panos Pictures; 16 (UP), Ulga/iStockphoto; 16 (LO), rimglow/iStockphoto; 17 (UP), David Cheskin/PA Wire URN:6237815 (Press Association via AP Images); 17 (LO), Steve Stankiewicz; 18, MSPhotographic/iStockphoto; 19, Ira Block/National Geographic Creative; 20, Eli Klein Fine Art; 21 (UPLE), Dasha Petrenko/Shutterstock; 21 (UPRT), claylib/iStockphoto; 21 (LO), David Quinn; 22-23, Frans Lanting/National Geographic Creative; 24 (LE), aphotostory/iStockphoto.com; 24 (RT), Maggie Steber/National Geographic Stock; 25 (LE), Photographed by Louis Gagnon, Bertram Lab, Carleton University; 25 (UPRT), attl/iStockphoto; 25 (LORT), lynnbcreative/iStockphoto; 26-27,

Janne Parviainen; 28 (UPLE & UPRT), NNehring/iStockphoto; 28 (LO), Eric Isselee/Shutterstock; 29 (UP), AP Photo/CTIA Wireless Foundation, Max Taylor; 29 (LO), Steve Stankiewicz; 30, Coffeemill/Shutterstock; 31, globestock/iStockphoto; 32, Kirill Oreshkin; 33 (UP), Mihai Simonia/Shutterstock; 33 (LOLE), David Quinn; 33 (LORT), Okea/iStockphoto; 34-35, Anurag Kumar/National Geographic Your Shot; 36 (LE), Frans Lemmens/Hollandse Hoogte/Redux Pictures; 36 (RT), GlobalP/iStockphoto; 37 (LE), Kostyantyn Ivanyshen/Shutterstock; 37 (UPRT), Ozja/Shutterstock; 37 (LORT), Syldavia/iStockphoto; 38-39, Gonzales Photo/Demotix/Corbis; 40 (UP), Romanenia/Shutterstock; 40 (LO), stocksnapper/iStockphoto; 41 (UP), AP Images/Primate Research Institute of Kyoto University; 41 (LO), Steve Stankiewicz; 42, fotoVoyager/iStockphoto; 43, Map courtesy Reto Stöckli, NASA Earth Observatory; 44, Esterio/Shutterstock; 45 (UPLE), STILLFX/Shutterstock; 45 (UPRT), Ulrich Knaupe/iStockphoto; 45 (LO), David Quinn; 46-47, Trần Bao Hòa/National Geographic Your Shot; 48 (LE), Neil_Burton/iStockphoto; 48 (RT), NASA; 49 (UP), lfmpereira/Shutterstock; 49 (LO), eAlisa/iStockphoto; 50-51, Berndnaut Smilde; 52 (UP), Splash/Lick Me I'm Delicious/Splash News/Corbis; 52 (LO), Ted Kinsman/Science Source; 53 (UP),

Noah Goodrich/Caters News Agency; 53 (LO), Steve Stankiewicz; 54, Dorling Kindersley/Getty Images; 55, Colleen Pinski/National Geographic Your Shot; 56, Victoria Wlaka Photography/National Geographic Your Shot; 57 (UPLE), FabioFilzi/iStockphoto; 57 (UPRT), Reuters/Courtesy of Intuitive Surgical/Landov; 57 (LO), David Quinn; 58-59, Chris Schmid/Aurora Photos/offset.com; 60 (LE), Nicolas Bouvy/epa/Corbis; 60 (RT), Praisaeng/Shutterstock; 61 (LE), Sebastian Janicki/Shutterstock; 61 (UPRT), Sebastian Janicki/Shutterstock; 61 (LORT), Jeff Fullerton/iStockphoto; 62-63, Thomas Dressler; 64 (UP), Jason Edwards/National Geographic Creative; 64 (LO), Alexander Raths/Shutterstock; 65 (UP), Barcroft Media via Getty Images; 65 (LO), Steve Stankiewicz; 66, Antonel/iStockphoto; 67, Andrew Rich/iStockphoto; 68, Shikhei Goh/National Geographic Your Shot; 69 (UPLE), James Steidl/Shutterstock; 69 (LOLE), Thomas R. Schultz; 69 (RT), jabiru/Shutterstock.com; 70-71, Larry Beard/National Geographic Your Shot; 72 (LE), AFP/Stringer/Getty Images; 72 (RT), GentooMultimediaLimited/iStockphoto; 73 (UP), MJTH/Shutterstock; 73 (LO), msk.nina/iStockphoto; 74-75, Kitra Cahana/National Geographic Creative; 76 (LE), ShutterWorx/iStockphoto; 76 (RT), Floortje/iStockphoto; 77 (UP), Alexander Natruskin/Reuters/Corbis; 77 (LO), Steve Stankiewicz; 78, SVM/